Other Titles of Interest

PUBLIC ADDRESS
LOUDSPEAKER SYSTEMS

by

Vivian Capel

BERNARD BABANI (publishing) LTD
THE GRAMPIANS
SHEPHERDS BUSH ROAD
LONDON W6 7NF
ENGLAND

PLEASE NOTE

Although every care has been taken with the production of this book to ensure that any projects, designs, modifications and/or programs etc. contained herewith, operate in a correct and safe manner and also that any components specified are normally available in Great Britain, the Publishers do not accept responsibility in any way for the failure, including fault in design, of any project, design, modification or program to work correctly, or to cause damage to any other equipment that it may be connected to or used in conjunction with, or in respect of any other damage or injury that may be so caused, nor do the Publishers accept responsibility in any way for the failure to obtain specified components.

Notice is also given that if equipment that is still under warranty is modified in any way or used or connected with home-built equipment then that warranty may be void.

© 1990 BERNARD BABANI (publishing) LTD

First published — October 1990

British Library Cataloguing in Publication Data:
Capel, Vivian
    Public address loudspeaker systems.
    1. Public address systems
    I. Title
    621.3892

    ISBN 0 85934 237 9

Printed and Bound in Great Britain by Cox & Wyman Ltd, Reading

Notice

LISCA is a copyright design, but licence is granted by the author to each first purchaser of this book only, to install a LISCA system or any variant. Commercial licences may be granted by negotiation.

In return, the author would like to hear from any readers installing LISCA, giving details of the installation and observations on its performance so that information can be collated to guide future development. Please write c/o the publishers.

About the Author

His work as an audio, television and radio engineer with several service organisations including that of Philips, gave him a wide experience expanded by his practical and advisory work on large public address systems. As a violinist who has played in several amateur orchestras, he is able to combine the viewpoint of both technician and musician.

His articles have appeared in the technical press for over thirty years, and he is the author of a dozen books on audio, acoustics and related subjects. He now works full time as a writer and audio consultant.

Preface

A visit to many halls where there is public address speech reinforcement, often reveal systems that range from barely adequate to the downright dreadful. Long-suffering audiences put up with what they come to accept as 'public address sound', and sometimes even believe it to be good — until they hear a really good public-address system elsewhere.

Those responsible are often aware of problems, call in local 'experts', and buy expensive new equipment with little or no improvement. In most cases the fault lies with either unsuitable microphones or a poorly designed loudspeaker system. This is often the result of the system being installed by someone with electronic experience but no knowledge of acoustics; both skills are required to design a successful p.a. installation.

Among common defects is the use of the outmoded ceiling matrix of loudspeakers with its inherent boomy unnatural effect and chopping up of higher speech frequencies due to mutual interference. Similar multi-unit systems were abandoned by professional engineers some 30 years ago, yet they are still being fitted by unqualified installers. Also to be seen are columns positioned without regard to their polar response, thereby losing their major advantage of directing sound precisely where it is required.

We here explore the acoustic properties of various systems and give a full description of LISCA, the line source ceiling array which overcomes the disadvantages of all other systems and gives exceptionally clear and natural sound. Practical step-by-step instructions are given on how a LISCA system can be designed for a particular hall, and how to construct and install it. Also covered are: low-impedance matching, 100V systems, mixed systems, transmission lines and hearing-aid induction loops.

Vivian Capel

Contents

Chapter 1

THE MOVING COIL LOUDSPEAKER

The basic unit of most public-address systems is the moving coil loudspeaker. It makes use of a principle patented as far back as 1898 by Oliver Lodge, and later developed into a workable loudspeaker by Rice and Kellogg, which they patented in 1925. It says much for their design that it has changed only in details and materials used, since then.

While most people know what a loudspeaker looks like, and many have a rough idea how it works, the public-address man should be thoroughly familiar with it, its various parts, and how they function. A cross section of a typical unit is shown in Figure 1.

Cone Surround

The cone is usually made of paper and is fixed around its outer edge to the chassis (sometimes called frame) either directly or by means of a flexible roll of cloth, sponge or rubber. The roll can be either a *half-roll out* in which the roll faces outward or a *half-roll in* whereby it faces inward toward the back of the speaker. When the cone is fixed directly to the chassis, there are corrugations around the perimeter; these can be of *two sine rolls*, a *single sine roll* or a deeper *accordion pleat.*

The purpose of these is to permit forward and backward motion of the cone while holding it firmly against any sideways movement, but they also have another important function. When the cone vibrates, ripples can spread out from the centre like ripples in a pond when a stone is thrown in. If you observe pond ripples closely, you will notice that if they encounter a hard boundary such as a stone sidewall, they are reflected back across the surface, but if they meet a soft perimeter of reeds, grass or mud, they are mostly absorbed and very few are reflected.

In the case of the loudspeaker cone, reflections produce spurious cone motion that is not in response to any electrical output from the amplifier. So a necessary function of the

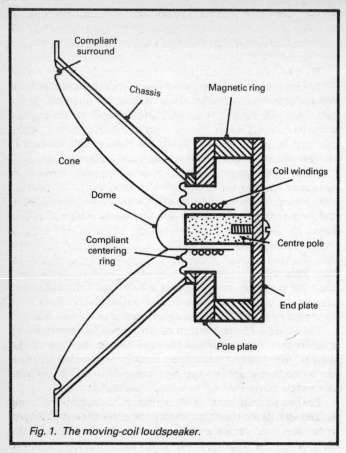

Fig. 1. The moving-coil loudspeaker.

surround is to absorb and dampen such vibrations, so preventing reflections.

Cone Materials

If ripples and flexures which can colour the reproduction even before they may be absorbed by the surround, are to be avoided, the cone should be made as stiff as possible. When a pond surface is frozen hard, ripples, waves or any other disturbances are not possible. Similarly, a perfectly stiff cone would move like a piston, backwards and forwards without any flexures, and so should radiate air pressure waves that are a perfect replica of the electrical currents flowing through the speaker circuit.

So why not make the cone of metal such as aluminium? They have, but that exchanges one set of problems for another. Metal cones tend to 'ring' when subject to vibration, like a bell when it is struck. Most hollow metal cans or boxes give a distinctive sound when flicked with a striker such as a pencil. An ideal loudspeaker cone should have no sound of its own at all, if it has, it will colour the sound it reproduces.

Another problem is inertia. The loudspeaker cone must accelerate and decelerate very quickly in order to produce the very fast vibrations that make up a complex sound wave. To do this its mass must be low. A motor bike will always be away quicker from the lights than an articulated lorry in spite of having a much smaller engine, because its mass is a tiny fraction of that of the lorry. Metal cones, even aluminium ones, are much heavier than other materials commonly used, so they have a disadvantage here too. Honeycombed aluminium is light and about a thousand times more rigid than paper, but has not proved popular.

Polystyrene (same material as ceiling tiles) reinforced with aluminium foil is very light and rigid and has been used. Its snag is poor damping, it has a characteristic sound which is similar to that heard by tapping a ceiling tile held by one hand at its edge.

Bexetrene has been used in many hi-fi speakers being stiffer and more consistent in its characteristics than paper. It too has poor damping and needs to be coated with a plastic damper to tame it. Polypropylene is a more recently employed material and seems to have advantages as a cone material. It is light, has good self-damping, and is more rigid than paper.

So we come back to paper again. If you tap the paper cone of a loudspeaker, all you hear is a dull plop without any readily identifiable sound. This is the ideal for uncoloured reproduction. It is also very light, so the lack of stiffness is the only major snag. But we shall see later, this can be made use of and turned into an advantage.

The paper pulp stock from which loudspeaker cones are

made consists of wood and rag with various additives. One stock commonly used is *kapok*, which is produced from the hollow, oily fibres from the silk-cotton tree. These are especially light and strong and so are well suited for this purpose. Waxes, resins and fungicides are added.

Different characteristics can be imparted to the paper pulp stock by the length of the period for which it is beaten out in vats. Long periods produce short fibres which result in thin hard paper. Cones made from this are light and sensitive, though prone to resonances and poor damping. They are thus more suitable for low-fi transistor radio speakers. Short periods of beating give long fibres, that are more flexible and so less rigid. These are best suited for bass speakers or full-range controlled flexure speakers. It is thus possible to produce a paper for a specific cone application, which is another reason why paper is so popular with the manufacturers.

Cone Resonance

Every physical object has a fundamental resonance, that is a frequency at which vibration is greater than at any other for the same input of energy. Loudspeaker cones are no exception, which means that sound output at the resonant frequency is greater than at all others. The result is an uneven frequency response with an unnatural emphasis at that one frequency.

Below the cone resonant frequency, the sound output falls off at a rate of 12 dB per octave, so the frequency response in the bass region is determined to a considerable extent by the resonant frequency which should therefore be as low as possible.

The resonant frequency in free air is proportional to the square root of the reciprocal of the mass of the cone times the compliance of the suspension. The formula is:

$$f_r = \frac{1}{2\pi\sqrt{MC}}$$

in which M is the mass in grams and C is the compliance in metres per newton.

4

Compliance, which is the opposite hence the reciprocal of suspension stiffness, can be calculated from the cone mass and the resonant frequency as follows:

$$C = \frac{1}{(2\pi f_r)^2 \, M} \, .$$

Thus the compliance (the opposite of stiffness) and the mass should be high, but if they are too high other problems can arise. If the suspension is too compliant it may not keep the cone in place at high volume levels; while if the mass is too great, more energy is required to move the cone hence the speaker sensitivity is low and a large amplifier power is needed. The resulting high power dissipation in the coil causes heating with the undesirable effects noted later. Furthermore, as a large mass results in high inertia, the cone will not respond to rapid high frequency electrical signals.

Delayed Resonance

In addition to the resonance due to the effect of mass and compliance there is another. When ripples move outward from the centre of the cone to the rim and are not absorbed by the suspension they are reflected back to the centre. When the cone radius equals one wavelength or a multiple of it, the contours of the outward and reflected ripples coincide to produce an apparently stationary ripple or undulation of the cone. It is therefore known as a *standing wave.*

However, when the applied electrical signal ceases, the standing wave subsides, and the consequent cone motion radiates sound as it does so. Stored energy is thus released as spurious sound after the cessation of the signal. The effect is thus termed *delayed resonance*. For an 8-inch cone, the fundamental delayed resonance is at 4 kHz with harmonics at 8 kHz and 16 kHz. Efficient absorption by the cone surround is vital to minimise the effect.

Another spurious motion performed by some cones at certain frequencies is what is known as the *bell mode*. With this, opposite quadrants of the cone perform a flapping movement in unison, moving backwards and forwards together while the adjacent quadrants flap in the opposite directions. However, two lines at right angles across the cone which define the boundaries of each quadrant remain stationary relative to the flapping. This effect is due to lack of stiffness of the cone itself. Both these effects are considerably reduced in the elliptical loudspeaker.

At the centre of the cone is a dome that serves as a dust shield to prevent foreign particles from getting into the air gap and causing grating noises. At certain high frequencies, this dome sometimes moves independently of the cone, by reason of the compliance of the glued joint. It thereby exhibits its own resonant frequency which colours the reproduction. To avoid this in some models, the dome is molded as an integral part of the cone.

The Coil

Under the dome at the apex of the cone, lies the coil which consists of a number of turns of copper wire wound on a paper, composition, or aluminium cylinder.

To reduce the mass and thereby the inertia in high frequency speakers, aluminium is sometimes used instead of copper wire. To get as many turns as possible within the magnetic field, the wire is often of square, hexagonal, or ribbon configuration so permitting more turns per inch. Up to 40% greater conductor density can thereby be achieved, thus making for a more efficient motor system.

The standard impedance of the coil is 8 ohms, but 4-ohm and 16-ohm models are also available. Formerly, 3-ohms was the standard with 15-ohms for larger units, and these may still be encountered. The impedance consists of resistance and inductance in series, the resistance making up approximately two-thirds of the rated impedance. So the impedance of an unknown speaker coil can usually be determined by adding half as much again to the measured d.c. resistance.

The impedance may be considered a minimum value as it rises to a peak at cone resonance, and is usually above the rated value over most of its frequency range. This is of no great importance, but if the impedance should drop below the rated value it could cause overloading of the amplifier. Usually, a higher impedance than that of the amplifier output rating means less power, but often lower distortion, whereas a lower impedance produces higher distortion and possibility of amplifier overload with damage to its output stage.

Effects of Heat

The coil is heated by the current flowing through it, and the resistance rises by some 0.4% per degree C. Modern high-power rated speakers have coils wound on aluminium formers secured by high temperature epoxy resin adhesives and can withstand temperatures up to 300°C.

To minimise the effect of heat with high-powered music loudspeakers, various measures are employed to remove it quickly and reduce the temperature build-up. Large magnet assemblies help and sometimes these are blackened and provided with heat fins, but these are long term devices and have little effect on short term temperature variations produced by changing programme content. Treble units being smaller, have a lower maximum temperature than bass drivers, around 120°C. To aid dissipation, some units have gaps between the coil and magnet poles filled with colloidal ferromagnetic fluid held in place by the speaker's magnet. This also slightly increases efficiency and provides a measure of damping.

Heating problems are not usually encountered with public address loudspeakers that are intended for speech reinforcement. Speech is intermittent and lacks sustained bass frequencies, and most systems comprise a large number of units run well below their maximum power rating.

Cone Centering

At the back of the cone, there is a ring of flexible material with corrugations that is secured to the framework at its outer edge and to the cone at its inner. This has the important function of keeping the cone centered relative to the magnet poles. With cheap speakers as used in many transistor radios, the cone can become off-centre due mostly to warping of the thin metal frame so that the magnet poles are not true.

An off-centre cone produces distortion as it rubs against the magnet pole and can be tested for by standing the speaker on its magnet, face upward, and gently pressing the cone inward with the thumbs at opposite points across the diameter, then releasing it. Any rubbing can usually be felt, or heard if an ear is placed close to the cone. Sometimes though, trouble may be experienced from loose coil windings and these may not be detected by this test.

The Magnet

The magnet usually consists of a magnetic ring or rod mounted axially at the back of the speaker. The front pole is terminated by a steel rod pole piece which penetrates inside the coil, and is only slightly of smaller diameter so that the air gap between it and the coil is small. The rear magnet pole is extended by a cylinder or U piece towards the front, where it terminates in a plate with a hole or a ring that surrounds the outside of the coil, see Figure 2.

The magnetic field is thus concentrated between the internal rod and the inside of the surrounding hole and thereby through the coil windings. As with all magnets there is a small external leakage field, but modern speakers are designed to reduce this to a negligible amount. It may seem, when trying to attract a ferrous object with a speaker magnet, that the magnet is weak, but this is the reason. For the same reason there is little possibility of erasing a magnetic tape from the stray field of a modern speaker, this danger is often greatly exaggerated.

Connections from the coil are taken to a couple of soldered blobs on the cone from which highly flexible stranded copper wires connect to a terminal strip on the speaker frame. These wires must never be tight nor must they loop down to touch the cone at any other than their soldered connection; they must be completely free of all obstruction. Failure to ensure this could result in buzzing noises as the cone vibrates.

Dedicated Drivers

To achieve an extended low-frequency response, the mass of the cone needs to be large so that it has a low resonant frequency. Furthermore, its diameter should also be large because the efficiency of the cone falls with decreasing diameter at low frequencies. However, to obtain a good transient and high-frequency response the cone should be small and light.

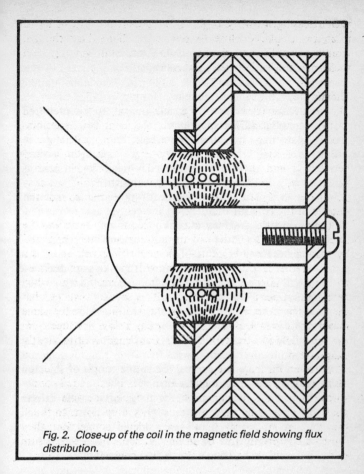

Fig. 2. Close-up of the coil in the magnetic field showing flux distribution.

These conflicting requirements have led to the general use of separate drivers for treble and bass, commonly known as tweeters and woofers. The signal is split into two, one containing all the high frequencies and the other the low by a filter circuit termed a *crossover network*, and fed to the respective drivers. A mid-frequency range speaker is also used in some models, and some have super-tweeters and sub-woofers to extend the range to inaudibility in the treble and bass.

Controlled Flexure

There are many disadvantages in using separate bass and treble units. These arise from their spatial difference which causes mutual interference and cancellation effects, distortions caused by the crossover circuit, and difficulties in maintaining balance over the whole frequency and power range. Even for hi-fi purposes, the use of a single unit is to be preferred.

With public-address speech reinforcement systems, single loudspeaker units to cover the whole frequency range are almost universal. Now in theory as we have seen, a single speaker cannot cover a wide frequency range, yet in practice they actually do. How then do they manage it?

The answer lies in the flexure of the cone at different frequencies. At high frequencies, the central area of the cone responds, but the rest of the cone remains stationary because of its inertia. This independent movement of the central area is possible because of flexure of the non-rigid cone around that area. As the frequency decreases, so larger areas of the cone are brought into play, until at low frequencies the whole cone is in motion (see Figure 3).

This effect occurs to some extent with most loudspeakers, but some cones are specially made to exploit it. These have curved sides, and the flexure points are designed into them so that a smooth coverage of a wide frequency range is achieved. They often have a small horn fixed to the centre of the cone to increase efficiency at high frequencies.

Although not having quite the range of separate drivers, it is by no means inadequate, a typical specification being 40 Hz − 17 kHz. Such full-range drivers as they are called, avoid all the problems of having multiple drivers, and have few vices. They have thus much to commend them for hi-fi use. For public-address though, ordinary loudspeaker units have a perfectly adequate frequency range, and extended range units besides being an unnecessary expense could cause feedback problems.

Cone Velocity and Radiation Resistance

The effect of cone inertia is to limit its acceleration, just as a heavy lorry which has considerable inertia, cannot get away so quickly from the lights as a light car. As the frequency rises

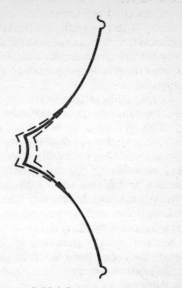

Fig. 3. *Controlled flexure. At high frequencies the central areas of the cone move independently of the rest. The higher the frequency, the smaller the active area. Thus all frequencies are effectively radiated without use of separate tweeters.*

and the cone makes more excursions per second its speed needs to increase to maintain the same amplitude. This requires more power, but if the power is constant the speed must also be constant. So when the frequency rises, the amplitude of the cone excursions must decrease to maintain the same speed. This means that the response diminishes as the frequency increases, an effect which without compensation would give a very poor treble reproduction.

Fortuitously, and by one of those rare quirks of the laws of physics, there is another defect in the way sound is propagated by a loudspeaker cone that almost exactly cancels the effect of the first. This is *radiation resistance*. At low frequencies the cone is an inefficient sound radiator. It pushes the air out of the way instead of compressing it into a sound wave.

11

As the frequency increases, the air does not move aside fast enough to avoid compression but offers a resistance to the cone and so produces sound. The higher the frequency up to a certain point, the greater the radiation resistance and the more efficient the air coupling to the cone. Thus the acoustic output rises and exactly compensates for the diminishing cone excursions.

The compensating effect works up to a point when the radiation resistance is at a maximum and cannot increase further. This frequency range is termed the *piston region* of operation. Above this the response begins to fall off because the cone excursions due to velocity effect continue to decrease. However, cone flexure effects maintain the response further, and also the beaming effect at high frequencies increasingly concentrate the sound in front of the cone. Thus a useful response continues well above the piston region so making full-range single-unit speakers viable.

The piston region transition point is dependent on the diameter of the cone. For a flat disc radiator in a true infinite baffle, the relation between the transition frequency and the cone diameter is:

$$f = \frac{68,275}{\pi d}$$

in which d is the cone diameter in centimetres.

It can thus be seen, that there is a lot more to the moving-coil loudspeaker unit than may at first appear.

Chapter 2

BEING BAFFLED

When the cone of a moving coil speaker moves backwards and forwards it generates two separate sound waves, one at the front and the other at the back. Air is compressed in one direction while that in the other is rarefied. The two waves are thus said to be out of phase.

Phase is often described by comparing it with an imaginary line rotating around a central point, a device termed a *vector*. At a half-revolution which is 180°, the signals are displaced by one half-cycle, and are totally out of phase. At 90°, the signals are a quarter-cycle displaced and are said to be in *quadrature*. Two out-of-phase signals can be represented by two lines drawn one from the end of the other at the appropriate angle, and if they are drawn to scale with the length representing signal amplitude, the value of the resulting signal (the *resultant*) can be found. This is done by simply joining the end of the second to the start of the first by a third line to form a triangle. The length of the third line then gives the amplitude of the resultant, see Figure 4.

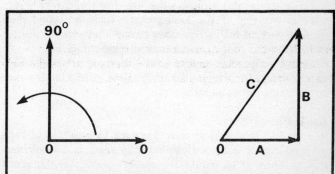

Fig. 4. Vectors. Signal amplitudes are indicated by line lengths and phase by angles. During a complete cycle the line rotates through 360°. If two signals A and B are drawn one from the end of the other, the phase angle and amplitude of the resultant is determined by joining line C.

Phase differences are often present when two or more loudspeakers are operating in close proximity as they are in most public-address systems. If one speaker should be connected the opposite way to an adjacent one, its cone will be travelling backward while the other is going forward, so one produces a compression while the other generates rarefaction. Where they meet there is mutual interference and cancellation, resulting in zero or a very low sound level.

Interference and Cancellation
Interference can produce both reinforcement and cancellation. Where there are multiple speakers, there is usually a complex reinforcement and cancellation pattern of various frequencies at different locations.

When a listener is equidistant from two in-phase loudspeakers, there is reinforcement at all frequencies, but when he moves away from this point and is nearer one unit than the other, the interference varies with frequency. There is cancellation when the sound path lengths differ by 0.5 wavelength, 1.5 wavelengths, 2.5 wavelengths, 3.5 and so on; and reinforcement when the difference is a complete wavelength or a multiple. The result is a series of troughs and peaks in the frequency response.

Cancellation also occurs when the front and rear waves meet at the rim of the loudspeaker. Radiated sound then consists only of high frequencies having a wavelength shorter than the radius of the cone, as one or more complete cycles of these are propagated before cancellation occurs at the rim. This accounts for the familiar tinny effect when a loudspeaker is operated without a baffle.

The Baffle
It is evident then that some means must be provided to keep the two out of phase waves physically apart, and an obvious way to do so is to mount the speaker on a large flat board termed a baffle. They still meet at the edge, but they have further to go and so longer wavelengths can be propagated before cancellation takes place. Thus the bass response is extended compared to that of an unmounted speaker, as shown in Figure 5. The straightforward baffle has many

14

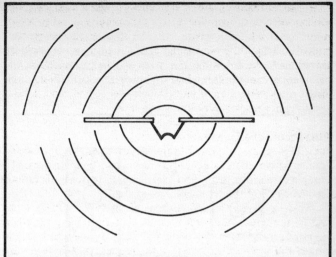

Fig. 5. Flat baffle. Extends front/back path along which out-of-phase sound waves merge and cancel, thereby lowering frequency at which cancellation occurs.

advantages, among which is the lack of air resonance that produces the colouration inherent with an enclosure. Also panel resonances and vibrations common with cabinets are minimal.

One potential snag is that because of the time taken for the rear sound waves to reach the edge of the baffle, delays occur which at some frequencies can mean that a compression wave from the rear is propagated at the same time as the next compression wave from the front, so that they actually reinforce each other. At other frequencies the opposite occurs and cancellation takes place.

Just as with two adjacent loudspeakers, reinforcement occurs at wavelengths that are 0.5, 1.5, 2.5 . . . times the radius of the baffle, whereas cancellation takes place at whole multiples, 1.0, 2.0, 3.0 . . . times the radius. The effect is a very uneven frequency response with alternate peaks and troughs throughout its range.

It can be easily avoided though by simply mounting the speaker off centre on the baffle. There is thus no uniform radius and the cancellation and reinforcement effects are smoothed out. A rectangular baffle with the speaker off centre gives good results, but a circular or square one with the speaker at the centre is the worst possible case, see Figure 6.

Fig. 6. A speaker in the centre of a square baffle has an almost equal radius to the baffle edge, so cancellation occurs at whole multiples of the radius wavelength and reinforcement at half multiples. This effect is avoided in a rectangular baffle where the radius is not the same in all directions, thus smoothing out the effects of cancellation.

The big problem with an open baffle lies in the size of baffle needed to procure an adequate bass response. To achieve a flat response down to 45 Hz, requires a baffle with the shortest radius of 25 ft (7.7 m). That means a width and height of more than 50 ft, which is obviously impractical.

Looking at more practical dimensions, a 2 ft radius which is a 4 ft width or height would be about the maximum. This would start to roll off at 280 Hz which is rather high, but an ameliorating factor is that the bass fall-off is only 6 dB per octave. This means a −6 dB response at 140 Hz, and a −12 dB level at 70 Hz. The bass response of most enclosures drop sharply below their rated limit, so with a baffle of this size there is at least some response in the bass though not very much. Fortunately though, an extended bass response is unnecessary for speech, and in fact is detrimental to clarity and likely to provoke feedback. Most p.a. operators cut the bass to a certain extent, to avoid these effects.

Adding Sides

The dimensions of a baffle can be practically increased by adding sides, a top and a bottom. The front-to-back path is thereby extended slightly improving the bass response.

A further step is to add a back in which a number of slots have been cut. This adds to the front-to-back path and the slots serve as an acoustic resistance to the rear wave. So the bass is noticeably increased. However, the enclosed space has a more pronounced resonance which affects the reproduction. Alternatively, the back can be solid thus blocking off the rear wave completely. However, the back itself can resonate, unless it is of substantial thickness and screwed at frequent intervals around its perimeter.

Really, we now have a conventional loudspeaker cabinet such as used for ante rooms, and other auxiliary locations. These come in various shapes and sizes including a V shaped configuration that contains two units angled downward, one on either side. This is intended for corridors or other narrow areas.

From the viewpoint of an effective baffle, ceiling-mounting scores highest because the ceiling becomes the baffle. It thus has a very large area with virtual total separate of rear and front waves, a true infinite baffle. In theory it should therefore have an extended bass response if there are no air leaks in the mounting.

However, this is not important for public-address work and in fact as we have seen, is not really desirable. It has though the advantage of being free from box resonances, but as we shall see later, it can strongly excite the vertical auditorium resonance in the bass region. This together with its efficient bass response produces a very bassy effect and loss of clarity.

The LISCA array uses the ceiling as an extension of its own baffles and so has a good bass response, but it does not excite the vertical resonance. It thus has a balanced tonal effect which can be tailored if required by a little bass cut at the amplifier.

17

Chapter 3

PUBLIC ADDRESS SYSTEM REQUIREMENTS

To design and install an effective public-address system we need to determine just what is needed, what we are aiming for and how it can be achieved. The first necessity is that the sound must be at a sufficiently high volume level to be comfortably heard at all parts of the hall by everyone with reasonable hearing. (The deaf can be catered for by an induction loop to be dealt with later.) This is the obvious requirement, but in a surprising number of installations it is not attained. In others it is considered to be the only one, and volume is heard at the expense of clarity.

Equally important though is the second: intelligibility. This is harder to effect and is the one that so many systems fall down on. The purpose of a public address system is to relay speech, to provide the communication link between the speaker and his audience. Nothing is accomplished by a system that enables the audience to hear the sound of the speaker's voice without understanding what he is saying, yet many do just that.

A third requirement, which though less important, is highly desirable if it can be obtained without detriment to the other two, is naturalness. Ideally, an audience should not be aware that a public address system is in operation at all, they should just hear what appears to be the natural sound of the speaker's voice coming from his own mouth at comfortable volume.

Adequate Sound Level

Going back to that first requirement, it is governed to a large extent by the great bugbear of all public address systems, feedback. When the level of sound from the loudspeakers picked up by the microphone exceeds a certain value the system goes into oscillation giving the all-too-familiar howl. Just below this level, there is incipient oscillation, whereby reproduced sounds are accompanied by 'ringing', a decaying oscillation which is heard during pauses after phrases and sentences. Even below that, feedback still can affect the reproduction by colouring speech with a degree of reverberation which reduces intelligibility.

Thus, the operating level must always be kept well below oscillation level. But this means that the volume may be insufficient, especially with quietly spoken speakers, or those that ignore the microphone. These, like the poor, seem to be always with us! The alternative is to so design the system that feedback oscillation starts at a higher volume level; we then say that we have raised the feedback point.

Feedback reaches the microphone via two possible routes: one is direct from the loudspeakers, and the other is reflected from the walls of the auditorium; we call this indirect sound. The first can quite easily be prevented by using directional loudspeakers such as columns, or other types of line-source systems aimed so that their output is directed into the audience and away from the microphone.

The second route is less easy to prevent, in fact it cannot be completely eliminated. It can be minimised by arranging the loudspeakers so that no sound is radiated directly at the walls and ceilings thereby reducing wall reflections. This is well achieved in LISCA, the system later described.

Another effective way of reducing the pickup of indirect sound is by using super-cardioid or hyper-cardioid microphones. As indirect sound comes back to the microphone at all angles, any rejection of sound from angles other than that of the desired source, reduces feedback.

The directivity of microphones is classified as *omni-directional* (picks up sound from all directions); *cardioid* (having a heart-shaped polar response, with a high rejection of sounds from the rear, but reduces sounds from the side by only a half [−6 dB]); *supercardioid* (which has a greater side rejection than the cardioid); and *hypercardioid* (having the maximum side rejection, though there may be less rear rejection than the cardioid; even so it has the greatest total off-axis rejection).

The cardioid is only suitable for mounting on a microphone stand with its rear always toward the auditorium. If the microphone is likely to be used in the hand or on a stand so that its side is toward the auditorium, a supercardioid or hypercardioid must be used. As this mode of use is always probable, it is best not to use cardioids at all.

Another important feature of the microphone which is not generally appreciated is that it should have a flat frequency response without peaks. Oscillation is initiated whenever a response peak exceeds the feedback point even though the general level is well below it. So the operating level is determined by the amplitude of the highest peak in the response.

Thus, if there are no peaks, the general level can be elevated to the feedback point before oscillation commences, and a higher sound level can be sustained. Another effect is that microphones with a flat response are slow to start oscillating even when brought up to feedback level, while those with a peak oscillate readily. So flat-response microphones are easier to control and permit higher volume levels.

It might be mentioned here that unfortunately, microphones having both a supercardioid or hypercardioid characteristic, and a flat frequency response are few and far between. For example all moving-coil units have a response peak due to the mechanical resonance of the coil and diaphragm, though the better ones are damped to a certain extent.

Ribbons generally have a flat response but there are not many of these about. The Beyer M260 is a classic example, having both a flat response and hypercardioid polar characteristic, but it is rather expensive. Some electret microphones are good, having high directivity with reasonable smooth response, but not all are, most are only cardioids and have peaks in their treble response. A particularly good model is the Altai EM 506 which is robustly made and is also inexpensive.

Intelligibility

Reducing feedback then is the biggest factor in obtaining sufficient volume, but now we will take a look at the second requirement, intelligibility. This really is the most important of all; moderate or even low volume speech that is intelligible, is far better than high volume speech that is not. So we need to understand what makes speech intelligible in order to know how to preserve it in reproduction.

Speech consists of two main parts, vowels and consonants.

In general, vowels are easily recognized because they are distinctive, and the long vowels at least occupy more time than other speech sounds. They also consist mostly of the lower speech frequencies.

Consonants are less easy to identify because many are so similar, they occupy only a short time, often being little more than transients, and they are made up of the higher speech frequencies of 1–2 kHz. Yet, because there are so many more of them than vowels, they are of major importance. They distinguish between the many different words that share the same vowel sounds and so otherwise sound the same.

So, intelligibility depends to a great extent on the clear and accurate reproduction of consonants. Impaired consonants can render speech quite unintelligible. Yet it is the consonants that often suffer in a poor public address system, as we shall see. Added to this is the fact that many speakers fail to enunciate consonants adequately, especially at the ends of their words. The glottal stop, common in some parts of the country, in which the 't' sound is omitted completely, is a case in point.

The classic example of misunderstanding due to poor intelligibility is the story of a message said to have been relayed by word of mouth during a battle in the Great War. It started as 'we are going to advance, send reinforcements'. By the time it got back to HQ it had become: 'we are going to dance send three and fourpence'. The vowel sounds were practically unchanged, it was the consonants that suffered, so causing such a drastic change of meaning — and bewilderment to the top brass!

The ear has among its many remarkable design features, the ability to fill in missing sounds, even complete syllables, in a familiar context so that it hardly notices that they are missing. For example, if you heard a chairman at a meeting say: 'Good eve—ing ladies and gene——men, it gives me grea— pleasu— to int—duce our speak— for this eve—ing'. There would be little doubt that almost everyone in the audience would understand him. But if he was announcing an unfamiliar topic and a speaker with an unusual name, missed syllables would likely mean misunderstanding.

This is a problem when trying to assess the intelligibility of a public address system. In hearing a test passage read over the system, how can it be determined what was actually heard and how much was aurally filled in?

The solution employed in standard intelligibility tests is to use monosyllabic nonsense words. A number of volunteers sit in various parts of the auditorium and write down what they think they heard, while a speaker reads out a list of nonsense words. The degree of accuracy gives the PSA (percentage articulation index) of the system. A 100% is unheard of and never attained; 95% is considered the maximum and not often achieved. Around 80% will result in reasonably good audience comprehension, but at 75% concentration will be necessary. Below 65% indicates poor intelligibility. A realistic aim is thus to get the PSA somewhere between 80% and 95%, above 90% if possible.

Another factor affecting intelligibility is hearing impairment due to the age of the listener, known as presbycusis. Hearing declines with age, but more so at the higher frequencies. The aural response of a 50-year old to frequencies of 4 kHz is some 10 dB down on what it was at 20. At 60 it drops to about −24 dB, while at 2 kHz it is 12 dB down, and 1 kHz is around −6 dB. The low frequencies are relatively unimpaired.

Deterioration also occurs if the subject has been exposed to long periods of excessive noise, at work or elsewhere, but irrespective of the type of noise, the impairment starts at 4 kHz, and spreads lower.

So the higher speech frequencies which are the ones most needed to reproduce consonants so necessary to achieve good speech comprehension, are the ones most affected both by advancing age and hearing damage.

From this it is evident that while public address systems that distort the high frequency band or emphasize the low, will have generally poor intelligibility, some in the audience will be more affected than others. Many, especially the young, may be unaware of any deficiency, but older ones may experience considerable difficulty in comprehension.

It can be seen from all this that it is not easy to judge how good a system is by just giving a short listening test. It may seem quite good to an under 40-year-old with a good speaker, but how will it sound with a poor speaker to an older person? One way to assess it is to conduct a PSA with persons of various ages, but this is not always practicable. The best way is to design the loudspeaker system along sound acoustic principles from the beginning.

Naturalness

Natural sounding public-address is a goal to be achieved if at all possible. With large installations it is less easy to attain than with smaller ones, but much can be done in both cases to make the sound natural. Ideally it should seem as if the sole source of the sound is the speaker, except that his volume is sufficient to fill the hall.

In small or medium-sized halls the first couple of rows need only moderate sound reinforcement, because the speaker is only a few feet away, and his natural voice can be heard directly. Such reinforcement should appear to come from the speaker, so the source should ideally have a centre-front location. Further back, there is little direct sound from the speaker and all comes from loudspeakers, but it still should sound as though it is coming from the platform. A frontal source is therefore necessary, and a central location in the same plane desirable.

This is difficult to achieve with conventional systems. With column speakers, a frontal source location in the same plane is indeed obtained, but for the majority of the audience, the source is at the side, where the column is usually installed. For the ceiling matrix system matters are much worse as the sound comes from overhead and for many locations, from behind. The LISCA system described later, does give front-centre sound for the whole audience, and reduced volume for the first rows.

In addition to natural source location, the sound should have a natural tone, being free from boominess, harshness or other tonal defects. Apart from possibly impairing intelligibility, such deficiencies make the audience constantly aware of the sound system, rather than the speaker.

It may be thought that as long as the sound can be heard and understood, that is all that matters; the location and tone are unimportant. While they are secondary, they are nonetheless important. Deviation from natural sound can cause subconscious mental fatigue, and reduce the attention span of the audience. So, the quality of naturalness should never be underestimated.

There then we have the basic requirements, we can now go on to see how they can be achieved in the design of the loud-speaker system.

Chapter 4

SOUND PATTERNS

Many of the principles of sound proagation and the patterns
it forms can be illustrated by means of ripples in a large
rectangular tank full of water. There are of course several
differences: the sound wave is a compression disturbance
whereas the ripple is a lateral one, and the sound wave propa-
gates through three dimensions while the ripple moves only
in two. However although simplified, a lot can be learned
about acoustics, and the behaviour of invisible sound waves
which are not easy to visualize, from the observation of ripples
on water.

Attenuation With Distance

Let us then imagine a number of corks floating in different
positions, and a tap is dripping at one end. Each drip produces a circular ripple which expands, causing the corks to
bob up and down as it passes. Those near it respond noticeably, but the more distant ones move to a much lesser extent.
The furthest may hardly be affected at all if the tank is large,
as the ripple decreases in amplitude while it expands.

This illustrates the first basic principle of sound wave
propagation from a single point source. The wave amplitude
decreases with distance, which could be expected, but the
reason why it does so probably may not. It is not due to
friction or loss of energy due to particle motion. This does
play a part it is true, but a very small one. The main cause is
the way in which the wave expands to an ever increasing area.

To start with, only a small circle of water is affected, but as
the ripple expands, the circle gets larger, and an increasingly
greater amount of water is disturbed. The energy available at
the start must therefore be spread out over this greater area, so
the ripple amplitude decreases in proportion to the area it
covers. Eventually, it dies away completely.

The effect when a sound wave radiates out from a point
source, (called a monopole), is similar. In this case, as three
dimensions are involved it is an expanding sphere rather than

a circular ripple. More and more air must be moved as the sphere expands, so it diminishes in amplitude. Here, the area covered by a portion of expanding sound wave is the square of the distance from the source. Hence the sound intensity follows an inverse square law, decreasing to a quarter for a doubling of distance. It is expressed in decibels by: $10\log_{10}$ $0.25 = -6\text{dB}$.

Sound is more usually measured in SPL rather than intensity, (SPL: Sound Pressure Level). Using an electrical analogy, the intensity is the acoustic power in watts, whereas the SPL is the pressure equivalent to voltage. SPL is the square root of the intensity, so it decreases in direct proportion to distance, thereby halving for a doubling of distance. The formula is $20\log 0.5$ which is -6 dB.

This is for a point source in which sound expands as a sphere or semi-sphere. If confined to only two dimensions such as from a line-source, the attenuation is half of that from a monopole, and so is -3 dB for a doubling of distance.

For a single dimension such along a pipe, the attenuation is small as there is no wave expansion; the area of the pressure wave at the end is the same as at the start apart from small friction losses. Sound can thus travel a considerable distance along a speaking tube or ventilation duct with little loss.

We note that with our model of a single point source (see Figure 7), the wave considerably diminishes toward the far end of the tank, and it radiates in all directions. Thus, a single loudspeaker not only has insufficient volume to carry to the back of all except the smallest hall, but it also radiates backward toward the microphone thereby generating feedback at quite a low volume level. A single speaker or even two, one one each side of the hall would thus be quite inadequate.

Reverberation

One factor affecting intelligibility is reverberation, that is the amount of delayed sound caused by reflections from walls reaching the microphone and being re-amplified. Ripples propagated in a tank reach the edge then are reflected back to travel along a new path until they reach another boundary where they are reflected again. Soon individual ripples are lost in a general choppiness of the water surface. This has not been

Fig. 7. A monopole sound source radiates alternate high (solid lines) and low (dotted lines) pressure waves in all directions, rather like the ripples in a tank of water.

shown in the illustrations as it would have obscured the basic patterns.

If the tap stops dripping it takes a while for all the disturbances to cease and the surface to become smooth again. The amount of reverberation is specified in time, and is that in which the sound pressure dies away to a thousandth (−60 dB) of its former value. It can be several seconds in a large concert hall but should be no more than 0.75 seconds in an auditorium intended for speech.

The effect on intelligibility can be easily demonstrated by using a portable tape recorder. Record a passage read from a book or newspaper, first of all in your bathroom, then repeat it in the bedroom. When played back, the first recording will sound hollow, distant and difficult to follow due to the reflections from the tiled walls; while the latter will sound more immediate, close and easy to comprehend, because of their absence.

So a reverberant acoustic makes for poor speech intelligibility although it is good for music. The latter can be demonstrated if you wish, by recording yourself singing in both environments; the bathroom version will sound much better. (In the interests of domestic harmony, caution is advised before trying this test.)

Intelligibility, and feedback reduction, can often be improved by treating walls to make them more absorbent and less reflective. Especially it is important to treat the wall at the back of the platform, as reflections from this will rebound straight into the front of the microphone so nullifying its directional qualities.

The most practical and visually attractive way of doing this is to hang a curtain in deep folds from floor to ceiling along the whole length of the wall. In a number of cases, low volume and feedback problems have been completely solved by merely fitting such a curtain, when the replacement of expensive equipment had been contemplated.

Interference

A major factor is the phase differences and interference patterns caused by a multiplicity of sources radiating the same sounds, as we saw in Chapter 2. If the sound is propagated

Fig. 8. Multiple sources such as the ceiling matrix generate complex interference, with cancellation and reinforcement patterns varying at different positions.

from a number of loudspeakers, there will be some regions where the sound waves reinforce each other, but others where they cancel. These locations will vary according to the wavelength (the distance between one wave crest and the next), which in turn depends on frequency.

Let us get a visual idea of its effect by taking another look at the water tank. Imagine that we have a number of taps dripping in unison in a matrix arrangement as illustrated by Figure 8. The concentric rings of ripples expand out from each, but soon meet expanding adjacent rings. Corks close to any source respond more or less according to the ripples generated by it. Those equidistant between an adjacent pair or at the centre of a quartet are affected by two or four ripples simultaneously and so move in unison with the others.

However, at other points the corks will be hit by two, three or four ripples at varying intervals. The precise effect will depend on the wavelength between successive ones. The crest of some ripples will reach the corks at the same time as the troughs of others, so the net effect will be zero movement. In other cases crests will arrive in rapid succession causing chaotic movement of the cork which won't know whether it is going up or down.

What is the aural effect of using a matrix of loudspeakers? The eardrums of individual listeners move as do the corks, in sympathy with whatever pressure waves impinge upon them. Listeners that happen to be exactly equidistant between speakers hear the sound more or less as reproduced by a single one, but those in other locations receive out-of-phase sounds at various frequencies that mutually interfere with a sequence of cancellations and reinforcements that chop up the audio spectrum.

There is no question of the delays from different speakers producing echos, becausing the space difference is too small and the resulting delays too short. It would actually take a spacing difference of 50 ft or more to produce an audible echo. The ear/brain combination tunes in to the sound wave that arrives first, providing it is not more than 10 dB lower than one arriving later. So, all the sound appears to come from the nearest loudspeaker, and the listener is not conscious of sound from any of the others. This is known as the *Haas* effect.

The listener may thereby be deceived into thinking that he is actually receiving sound from only one source and that the others are having no effect. Yet this is not so, the quality of sound at the out-of-phase points is seriously impaired as some frequencies are cancelled, and other reinforced. He may not even be consciously aware of this, but will inevitably suffer poor intelligibility.

The Ceiling Matrix

Such multiple loudspeaker systems once were the standard because there was no practical alternative. They usually took the form of a number of cabinet units mounted along the walls or suspended from the ceiling. When the acoustically superior line-source columns were introduced they fell into disuse for auditoria and were used only for foyers, dining rooms and the like for background music and announcements. Now they have reappeared in some halls in the form of a matrix of rows of ceiling mounted loudspeakers.

Low frequencies which have long wavelengths are comparatively unaffected by this system. The difference in sound paths from two loudspeakers to a listener would have to be many feet to produce appreciable out-of-phase interference at long wavelengths. At such distances the volume level from the furthest one is too low to interfere.

It is when the sound path difference is only a matter of inches, and the sound levels are comparable, that significant interference occurs. For example, a sound path difference of 6.75 inches is equal to the half wavelength of 1 kHz, so at any location with such a difference there is cancellation of 1 kHz, also at 3 kHz, 5 kHz, 7 kHz and so on. At 2 kHz, there is reinforcement, also at 4 kHz, 6 kHz, 8 kHz upward. Below 1 kHz the sound level falls gradually from the bass to the first cancellation point at 1 kHz, see Figure 9.

This violent series of peaks and troughs, is called the comb filter effect, because the frequency response resembles the teeth of a comb. As noted before, the frequencies involved depend on the path length difference between two nearby loudspeakers and so varies from one seat in the auditorium to another. If the seat location is within a quadrant of four loudspeakers, the response is more complex, being the resultant

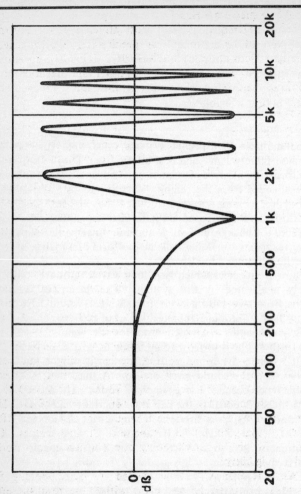

Fig. 9. Comb filter effect. With a sound path difference of 6.75 inches from two sources of equal amplitude, there is a fall-off to total cancellation at 1 kHz, followed by reinforcement at 2 kHz, further cancellation at 3 kHz and so on. Different sound path differences give different frequency points, but the pattern is the same. The result is chopping up of the higher speech frequencies with loss of intelligibility.

of all four pressure waves.

Now the frequency band most affected, is the very one that conveys the consonants in speech as noted previously, so it has a serious affect on intelligibility. It can also accentuate any tendency for a speaker to lisp, in those locations where reinforcement of the offending overtone occurs.

Auditorium Resonances

Every auditorium has three resonant frequencies. They are related to the half wavelengths corresponding to the height, length and width dimensions. These fundamental frequencies are thereby emphasized, and so produce peaks in the frequency response. In addition peaks are also produced at frequencies which are twice, three, and four times their value, such being known as the second, third and fourth harmonics. The harmonics usually decrease in intensity the higher they go, so although fifth and higher may be present they are relatively minor.

With most moderate sized halls, the length and width are too great to cause any problems. For example, a 50 ft dimension has a resonant frequency of 11 Hz, its second harmonic 22 Hz, the third 33 Hz, fourth 44 Hz and so on. A 25 ft dimension has frequencies of twice those values.

These are well below speech frequencies and so would not affect speech reproduction, but the height dimension, being much smaller is a different matter. A height of 9 ft has a fundamental resonant frequency of 62 Hz. The second, third and fourth harmonics are 124 Hz, 186 Hz, and 248 Hz. This is right among the lower speech frequencies and has the effect of emphasizing these at the expense of the higher ones. The result is to give a bassy, boomy effect which impairs clarity and intelligibility.

While resonances can be excited by corresponding frequencies generated in any plane within the resonant area, they are most strongly excited when the propagation is along the particular dimension. Hence, the worse position for a loudspeaker to energise the vertical resonance is pointing directly down from the ceiling. (It would be equally as bad to have it pointing up from the floor, but this is an unlikely position.)

It may be thought that the vertical resonance would be well damped by the people sitting in the audience, as people are highly sound absorbent. In addition the floor may be carpetted so adding further damping. However, this is not so for the following reason.

Any resonant body, whether it be a violin string or a column of air has regions of minimum particle vibration called nodes, and those of maximum vibration termed antinodes. To suppress such resonance, damping must be placed at the antinodes where there is maximum movement. It does no good at all to put it at the nodes as there is no movement there to stop.

In the case of a room or auditorium resonance, the node of the fundamental is half way along the dimension, while the antinodes are at the ends. Thus, the audience and the carpet do indeed dampen the fundamental of the vertical resonance. But the fundamental at around 60 Hz is not the problem. The second harmonic has its main antinode at the centre with two nodes at the quarter and three-quarter positions. The third harmonic has nodes at the sixth, half and five-sixth positions with antinodes at the third and two-third positions.

Thus the important second and third harmonic antinodes are at the half, and the third and two-third positions between ceiling and floor, so people-damping does not help much.

Added to all this, a further disadvantage of the ceiling matrix is that the row of loudspeakers nearest the platform radiate direct sound directly at the microphone and thereby encourage early feedback.

Finally, the desirable natural quality which was our third requirement for a public address system, is totally absent. The sound of the speaker's voice comes from above for everyone in the audience, and in many cases over the shoulder from behind. So there is a conflict between the spatial information fed to the brain from the eyes, and that from the ears. Though audiences can appear to 'get used to' this, it does subconsciously produce mental fatigue and lack of concentration and reduction of attention span.

Summarizing the multiple speaker system as exemplified in the ceiling matrix arrangement then, it produces interference patterns giving comb effect response at mid and high frequencies so obscuring the most important speech sounds and excites a strong vertical resonance at the lower speech frequencies; both of which reduce clarity and intelligibility. It also lowers the feedback point by radiating direct sound back at the microphone, and is quite unnatural in its effect. Little wonder that public address engineers gladly abandoned it over thirty years ago when the line-source column speaker came into vogue.

The reason for the re-emergence of the ceiling matrix is difficult to determine. There is certainly nothing really in its favour. Visual unobtrusiveness could be one reason, and a seemingly ability to give good overall area coverage could be another, although this is bettered by LISCA. Installers who fit them in halls and auditoria, instead of restricting them to single units in small areas, certainly betray a lack of understanding of acoustics, as they ignore the disadvantages we have described.

The line-source column which superseded the multi-speaker system will be described in the next chaper.

Chapter 5

THE LINE-SOURCE LOUDSPEAKER

The single-unit loudspeaker on a baffle behaves as a doublet or dipole in that it radiates sound in a figure 8 configuration with equal but out-of-phase lobes appearing from the front and the back. If the unit is in a sealed cabinet or is ceiling mounted, the rear lobe is suppressed, reduced or it is dissipated in the above-ceiling area, and it is only the front lobe that concerns us.

The lobe is spherical but unlike the monopole, the loudspeaker source is not at its centre, but at a point on its circumference. As we have seen, the expansion of the pressure wave through three dimensions produces a reduction of amplitude as the distance from the source increases. The rate is a halving of sound pressure for each doubling of distance, which is a reduction of 6 dB.

Another factor with the doublet is that the sound pressure decreases off-axis from the front. At the sides it is zero, and at any angle in between, it is equal to the cosine of the off-axis angle times the on-axis pressure. Or to put it mathematically:

$$SPL_2 = SPL_1 \cos a$$

where SPL_1 is the on-axis sound pressure level; SPL_2 is the off-axis value, and a is the angle.

Some practical examples of this are: at $25°$ the off-axis SPL is still 90%; at $41°$ it is 75%, and at $60°$ it is 50%; while at $75°$ it is 25%.

It can be seen from this that the level decreases only slightly over the first $25°$ deviation, but falls off increasingly rapidly thereafter.

If we arrange a number of loudspeakers in a vertical column the propagation pattern changes from a doublet to that of a line source. Sound is concentrated in the area immediately in front of the cones and there is little radiation above and below. Instead of an expanding sphere, we now have an expanding cylinder of sound. Being thus confined to two dimensions instead of three, the pressure expands over a smaller area and does not decline so rapidly with distance.

As we use the third dimension of distance from the source as a reference to compare sound intensities, it follows that the doublet radiates in the other two, vertical and horizontal, while the line source radiates in only one, the horizontal. The energy expended per unit of distance is therefore only half that of the doublet. So, the line source will radiate twice as far for the same SPL reduction as the doublet.

So while the sound pressure from a doublet drops 6 dB for each doubling of distance, that from a column drops 6 dB for each *quadrupling* of distance, or it drops 3 dB for a doubling of distance. This is a very useful factor and it means that a column can cover a much larger area than a doublet or single loudspeaker. It is especially useful for large auditoria in which it would be otherwise difficult to provide sufficient coverage for the central areas. It also means fewer loudspeakers so saving installation costs.

While the vertical dispersion is concentrated into a narrow beam thereby increasing the forward coverage, the side or horizontal dispersion is much the same as that of a doublet, and the SPL is approximately proportional to the cosine of the off-axis angle. It actually is flattened a little at the sides and the end is drawn out to give more of an oval configuration as shown in Figure 10. The side response thus falls off more rapidly after the 25° and this must be taken into account when siting column speakers to ensure that off-axis areas are sufficiently covered.

Divergence and Frequency

The divergent angle of the beam at its top and bottom, depends on the length of the line source, that is the distance between the two end drivers, and also the wavelength of the sound. A reinforcement and cancellation pattern occurs between the pressure waves produced by each unit in the column. Maximum reinforcement occurs along a line produced directly from the centre of the column, whatever the wavelength, but cancellation effects start on deviating from the on-axis line, and increase as the angle from that line

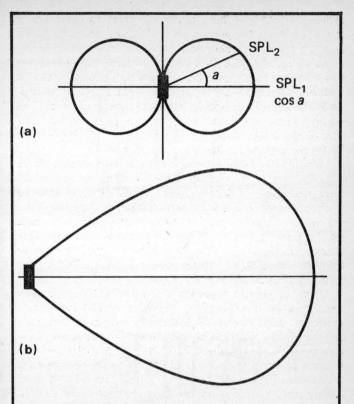

Fig. 10. (a) Polar diagram of doublet. Off axis sound pressure level is equal to that on axis, times the cosine of the angle.

(b) Polar diagram of a line source with rear lobe suppressed as with column loudspeaker.

widens. Cancellation is virtually total at about 58° when the column length equals the wavelength, so this is the effective maximum dispersion angle at that particular frequency. When it is twice the wavelength, the total cancellation, hence dispersion angle is 29°; when it is four times, the angle becomes 14.5°, and so on.

It can be seen from this that the divergence narrows for a particular column length as the frequency rises, until it reduces

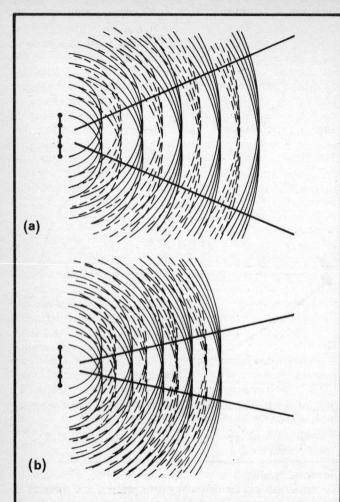

Fig. 11. *Vertical divergence of sound from a column loudspeaker. Interference and cancellation occurs where the high pressure (solid lines) and low pressure (dotted lines) meet. When the column length is equal to the wavelength as in (a), the dispersion angle due to cancellation is around 58°. At higher frequencies the angle narrows so that at half the wavelength (b), it is 29°.*

to form a parallel beam at the highest frequencies. To take a 5 ft column as an example, the frequency corresponding to this wavelength is 220 Hz, so the column has a 58° dispersion angle at that frequency. At 440 Hz, the angle is 29°, at 880 Hz, it is 14.5°, and at 1,760 Hz it is 7.25°.

It is noteworthy that any measurement of the divergence angle using mixed frequencies such as pink noise, gives a −6 dB value of around 14° for a 5 ft column. This is about the angle expected for a single 1 kHz frequency, which for a public address column is about halfway in its frequency range of 100 Hz − 12 kHz. It may not seem halfway, but there are approximately 3½ octaves below and above to those limits; that is why 1 kHz is often used for testing audio equipment. So the average divergence angle can be taken as 14° for a 5 ft column. It is narrower for a longer one, see Figure 11.

Incidentally, the mid point for hi-fi equipment which has a much greater range is 640 Hz, from which there are 5 octaves below to 20 Hz, and 5 octaves above to 20 kHz.

A beam that is only slightly divergent is another very useful feature of the column speaker because it can be directed where the sound is required, into the audience, and little is aimed at the walls and ceiling, thereby giving far fewer reflections. This gives better intelligibility and less feedback than single units. However, care must be taken in their siting and angling.

In some installations where few columns must cover a large area and it may not be possible to achieve optimum angling, the narrow beam at high frequencies may be considered a drawback. It may be thought desirable to widen it to give a greater angle of coverage. This may be especially so with long columns with which the divergence disappears at quite low frequencies.

Tapering
To obtain wider high-frequency divergence, some columns are frequency tapered. This means that only the centre drive units are fed with the full high frequency range, while adjacent ones are fed progressively less until the final ones are reproducing low frequencies only. Thus the effective column length is progressively shortened for increasingly high frequencies.

The means of achieving frequency tapering depends on the method of connecting the drive units. If connected in series, capacitors of increasing values can be connected across the outer loudspeakers with the largest value across the final ones. If connected in parallel, inductors of increasing values can be connected in series with the outer units, with the largest value at the ends, see Figure 12.

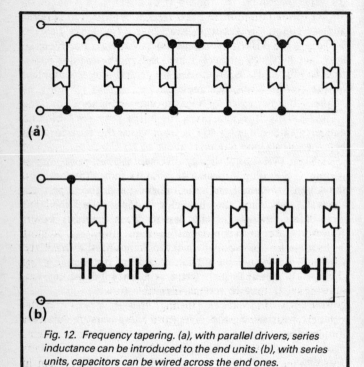

Fig. 12. Frequency tapering. (a), with parallel drivers, series inductance can be introduced to the end units. (b), with series units, capacitors can be wired across the end ones.

Longer columns having many units may have a series-parallel arrangement, and with these a combination of capacitors and inductors may be used.

Alternatively, a short line of tweeters can be mounted at the centre of the column alongside the main drivers, these being fed by a capacitor, or a more complex cross-over unit.

44

Some commercial units have used this method.

Small lobes usually appear at the start of the divergent beam at the top and bottom which are due to the off-axis radiation of the end units. These are sometimes suppressed by power tapering the column. This consists of feeding the maximum power to the central units, with a gradually reducing amount proceeding outward ending with minimum power at the ends.

One method of doing this in a six-unit column is to connect all the units in parallel, with the input going directly to the centre pair; an inductor is connected from these to each of the next, and a further inductor from those to the end ones. The column has thus a very low impedance and must be supplied via a suitable matching transformer.

The inductors also give frequency tapering so controlling the total vertical polar response by eliminating the lobes and giving a divergence angle that is more or less the same for both high and low frequencies.

With the more usual series connected column, power tapering can be achieved by shunting resistors across the final and penultimate drivers, a value equal to the driver impedance across the last ones, and one that is double the impedance across those previous. This wastes some amplifier power though. A cruder but more efficient method is to connect the last drivers in parallel, and these in series with all the others. They thus each produce a quarter of the output of the others. No power is lost, but it is not really tapering, just reducing the output of the final drivers.

Frequency and power tapering, though tidying up the technical polar response confers little real advantage. Neither non-divergent high frequencies or lobes pose any real problems if the columns are properly positioned. Most commercial units have neither, and there is little point in including them in amateur-built units unless for some special purpose.

Phasing

When constructing a column there are no special rules to observe as regards number of units or spacing, except that the spacing should be equal. Elliptical units are very suitable as they give length with little width and so when mounted vertically give the closest approach to a true line source. The power is divided between them, so six units each having a power rating of three watts will produce a column capable of handling eighteen watts. This is more than adequate in most cases.

If the drivers are the standard 8-ohms impedance, series connection will give a total of 48 ohms which seems rather high, however, it is common to use four columns in medium-sized halls (those seating about 200), so these connected in parallel would give a combined impedance of 12 ohms, which just under-loads an amplifier nicely from the 8-ohm tap and gives spare capacity for other auxiliary loads. But more of this in a later chapter.

Sometimes it is possible to purchase drivers cheaply that are of non-standard impedance such as 16 ohms. These permit considerable savings in cost especially if several columns are to be made. Six of these would give an impedance of 96 ohms, and four columns in parallel a combined total of 24 ohms. These could then be run from the 16-ohm amplifier tap.

When wiring the drivers inside a column, care must be taken to ensure that they are all connected in phase. Failure to do so will have some cones moving in while others are moving out, and cancellation will occur within the column. The out-of-phase unit detracts from rather than reinforces the output of the others. More than one unit out of phase can seriously impair the operation of the column.

If using new loudspeakers of the same model, one terminal will be found to carry a mark, either a red spot or a plus sign, to signify the positive terminal. For parallel connection, all the positives should be wired together and all negatives together. For series connection the positive of one unit must be connected to the negative of the next and so on until there is one free positive and one free negative terminal at the last two drivers.

The fact that one terminal is designated positve is just a convention to distinguish the two, there is no positive d.c. voltage or current involved.

If the loudspeakers have no markings, polarity can be checked by using a dry battery. A 4½ V box or 6 V lantern battery is quite suitable. Connect one pole of the battery to

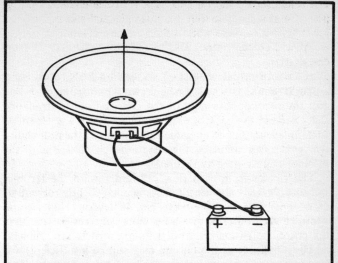

Fig. 13. Phasing an unmarked loudspeaker. Connect a battery to the terminals (not a car battery), and observe or feel the direction of cone movement. When it is forward, the positive of the battery is connected to the positive of the loudspeaker. Connect only momentarily to detect cone movement.

one terminal of the loudspeaker, and the other pole to a short length of wire. Touch the wire momentarily on to the other loudspeaker terminal and observe which way the cone moves. If the observed movement is too small to detect direction, place a finger lightly on the centre of the cone. It should then be possible to determine whether the cone moves in or out when the wire is contacted. Do not leave the battery connected for longer than necessary to establish direction of cone movement.

If the cone moved outward, the positive pole of the battery was connected to the loudspeaker positive and it should be marked accordingly. If it moved inward, then the battery negative was connected to the driver positive, see Figure 13.

After connecting all the units in the column, double check that the terminals are connected correctly; it is very easy to make a mistake, especially when wiring up several columns.

The inside should be filled with an absorbent material such as BAF (bonded acetate fibre) to dampen internal resonances.

Propagation

Let us return to our water tank to see how a pair of columns propagate sound in a hall. Imagine two taps dripping in unison near the two opposite sides of the tank and not far from one end. Around the back of each dripping point is a water shield which prevents ripples spreading backwards to the near end of the tank. This simulates the directional characteristic of the columns as illustrated by Figure 14.

The ripples from each flow outward toward the far end, and soon meet in the centre at some point slightly forward of the dripping places. The crests and depressions coincide and reinforce each other to give a far more coherent pattern than the chaotic situation observed with the matrix arrangement.

The amplitude at the far end may still be insufficient, so a second pair of taps are installed about a third the way along. They also have rear shields in the water behind each dripping point, and so produce only forward-going ripples. Reinforcement of the ripples from the first two occur, although the pattern is more complex where all ripples converge.

At most points in the tank, ripples come from a forward and side direction. None travel backwards. Back at the near end, although it is unaffected by direct ripples, the water is slightly disturbed by reflections from other parts of the tank. This corresponds to the indirect sound coming back to the microphones from the auditorium.

Applying the analogy to a hall with column loudspeakers, we achieve far less cancellation and interference effects than with the matrix system. Even when four columns are used, the pressure wave pattern is more coherent, hence intelligibility is superior.

The forward radiating sources give a general impression of sound coming from the front although it is also from the sides. Though not ideal it achieves a good degree of realism and is certainly better than having it come from over one's left shoulder! Furthermore, the columns are usually wall mounted and so the apparent sound source is on a similar elevation to

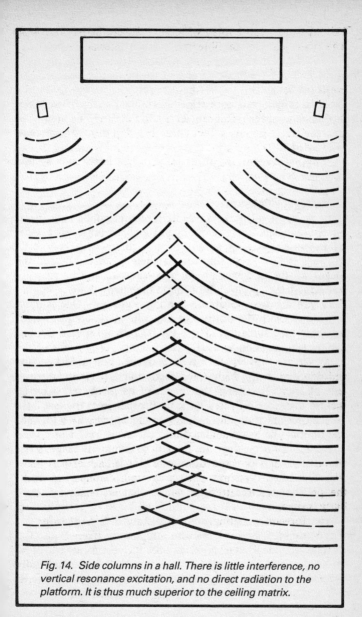

Fig. 14. Side columns in a hall. There is little interference, no vertical resonance excitation, and no direct radiation to the platform. It is thus much superior to the ceiling matrix.

the platform, which is much more realistic than an overhead source.

The lack of direct sound radiated back to the platform gives reduced feedback compared to the matrix arrangement. Also (although this cannot be demonstrated in the tank), the floor-to-ceiling resonance which has second or third harmonics in the low speech frequencies is not strongly excited. So the indistinct boomy effect often heard with matrix systems is avoided.

Thus is evident the superiority of the line-source system over the ceiling matrix.

Installing the Columns

Line source loudspeakers are often seen in public halls incorrectly installed, thereby producing poor results. The most common error is to mount them high up with very little forward tilt. They thus direct their beam right over the heads of the audience to hit the rear wall and be strongly reflected back up the auditorium to the microphone.

There are two possible mounting positions. One is quite low down, with the bottom of the column at shoulder height of the seated audience. There can be a slight forward tilt, but an upright position is usually satisfactory. The heads of the audience are thus within the range of the beam and its grazing incidence with the highly absorbent audience (sound absorbent of course!) ensures that much of its energy is exhausted before it can be reflected back up the hall from the rear wall.

The second position is somewhat higher but with a forward tilt so that the beam is aimed into the audience. This gives a greater absorption than the upright position. Its range is less though, as it is directed downward. It is like a torch beam being directed downward to the ground instead of along it. This is the preferred position where there are highly reflective wall surfaces such as stone, unfinished brick, or ceramic tiles.

Setting the correct angle of tilt is quite easy. It helps if a flat stick such as a rule can be temporarily fixed to the top surface of the column, pointing forward. Sit in the back row of the area it is intended the column shall cover, and note whether the stick is pointing downward so that you can see its top surface, or upward thereby revealing its under surface.

The correct angle is when the stick is pointing straight at you, if it is not, the tilt should be adjusted to achieve it. This does not take into account the divergence of the beam, which gives a margin for error.

Weatherproofing

Columns intended for permanent outdoor installations should be weatherproofed, and many commercial models are so designed. For the occasional outdoor assignment, the most practical weatherproofing can be provided by means of lie-flat polythene sheathing. This consists of a seamless polythene tube which can be obtained in rolls from many plastics merchants. It is available in various widths so a size can be chosen to accommodate the column. Cut a suitable length, fit it, then seal the top by turning it down and applying Sellotape. Leave the bottom open so that any condensation that develops inside can run out.

A casing of polythene seems to have no audible effect on the acoustic characteristics of the column, so, given the vagaries of British weather, it is a wise precaution to so protect the unit in any temporary outdoor installation.

Chapter 6

THE HORN LOUDSPEAKER

The horn loudspeaker was at one time the mainstay of the public address system. Now it is not often seen other than for announcements at sports stadia. It can have other applications, although these are rare. We will take a look at it though, if only to understand why it is not generally used today except for outdoor events.

The horn consists of a small moving coil unit usually with a metal diaphragm or cone feeding into a long tube which gradually increases in diameter until it opens out into a wide flare. The big advantage is its very high efficiency. It is the most efficient means yet devised of coupling the motion of a loudspeaker cone to the air with minimal loss.

Flares

The manner by which the horn increases in area can affect its performance. The simplest configuration is a cone, but it is by no means the best. Reflections can occur between the sides which cause interference and irregular frequency response as well as distortion. The ideal is an exponential horn by which the area increases according to an exponential law. This gives optimum air load matching and prevents internal reflections, see Figure 15.

The law governing the expansion of area, implies that there is a fixed relationship between the length of the horn and the size of the flare at its end. A large flare must have a long passage leading to it.

Another factor related to size is the frequency response. The shortest wavelength that the horn will reproduce is twice the diameter of the throat of the horn. The longest wavelength it will radiate is equal to twice the flare diameter. It is this last fact that gives rise to the big disadvantage. To obtain a response down to 100 Hz, a flare of 5.6 ft is required. For a 50 Hz response it would have to be 11.2 ft across.

The length of the horn needed for a specified flare and throat area is:

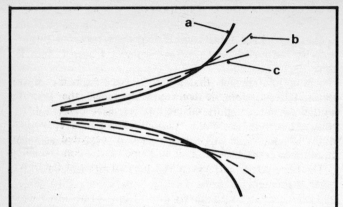

Fig. 15. The various horn flare configurations. (a) hyperbolic; (b) exponential; (c) conical.

$$L = \frac{4000\,(\log_{10} A - \log_{10} a)}{f \log_e}$$

in which L is the length of the horn in cm; A is the area of the flare, and a the area of the throat in cm^2; f is the lowest frequency; $\log_e$ is 0.4343.

A horn following a hyperbolic area increase gives a response to a lower frequency than that of the exponential horn, but the roll-off below it is more rapid. The area increase from the throat is more gradual, so the sound pressure is greater there, to fall off more rapidly near the flare. This pressure variation along the length results in distortion being generated.

Throat Design

The throat needs to be of as small an area as practically possible in order to obtain a good high frequency response, because as we have already seen the shortest wavelength the horn will produce is twice the throat diameter. However, the cone needs to be larger than this in order that it will function effectively, so this means that the area immediately in front of the cone must narrow down to the start of the horn proper. A region of high pressure is thereby created in front of the cone which could cause it to respond in a non-linear fashion and so produce distortion. To avoid this the pressure is equalized by a sealed chamber placed behind the cone.

Another problem is that sound pressure from the central and outer areas of the cone could arrive at the centrally located throat at slightly different times because of the difference in spacing from it. Cancellation effects at various frequencies could thereby occur. This is prevented by introducing a plug with holes in it in front of the cone to delay some of the pressure waves so that they all arrive at the throat at the same time.

The Re-entrant Horn
The big disadvantage of large size to achieve a reasonable bass response can be ameliorated to some extent by folding up the length. The result is known as the re-entrant horn and is illustrated by Figure 16.

The sound emerges from the throat and is deflected by a metal cone to the back of the flare from whence it emerges.

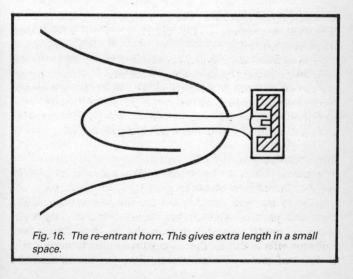

Fig. 16. The re-entrant horn. This gives extra length in a small space.

The flare can be either circular or rectangular. The former is more acoustically correct, but the latter can be more convenient to handle and mount.

Directional characteristics vary, but 60° to 100° is typical. One model which had a flattened flare and front diffuser was claimed to be omnidirectional. Power handling capabilities range from 5 to 40 watts.

While the re-entrant configuration reduces the size of the horn length to manageable proportions it does not help the flare size. As we have seen length and flare diameter are related, so increasing one without the other gives little advantage. Most horns have flares under 2 ft across, and so have little response below around 300 Hz. While this is sufficient to give intelligible speech, it makes it sound hard and tinny. This is of little consequence for short announcements at outdoor events, but for more prolonged use would be unacceptable.

Efficiency
However, their high efficiency, which can be over 80% (percentage of sound power produced from a given electrical power) compared to just a few percent of other types of loudspeaker, gives a very high output and so a long range as well as a high degree of audibility over ambient noise. They are thus well suited for announcements at sports stadia. A nest of horns mounted in an elevated position and suitably directed can cover all of the spectator area.

A point to remember is that a horn can be ear-shattering at close quarters, so one should never be mounted close to a spectator area. The power should be used to achieve a large area of coverage by forming a pool of sound from a height.

The efficiency can be used to good effect where power supplies are limited and high output is needed at the sacrifice of quality. Thus small re-entrant horns are used for battery powered hand-held loud-hailers.

Horns were once used in the cinema to give high power coverage over the whole auditorium for the relatively small amplifier powers that were then available. Amplifier power is no longer a limiting factor, but it is feasible to use a single horn in this way. The horn would have to have a flare of at least 6 ft diameter to give good low frequency response, and if mounted high above the screen, would cover the whole auditorium with no interference or blind spots.

Chapter 7

THE LINE-SOURCE CEILING ARRAY

For an indoor auditorium the choice of loudspeaker system has so far been between the ceiling matrix and the line-source. The ceiling matrix we have shown to have many disadvantages, in particular, interference and cancellation effects which play havoc with the frequency response in the all-important upper speech frequency region; excitation of the floor-to-ceiling resonance giving a bassy effect; unnatural sound location; and proneness to feedback.

The conventional line-source system using vertical columns avoids those problems and has been the preferred choice of sound engineers since their inception, but does not give an entirely natural source location. There is now another choice which offers advantages even over a system of columns, it is the Line Source Ceiling Array (LISCA).

Normally a column should never be used horizontally for two reasons. Firstly, the sharp cut-off at the ends would mean that coverage would be restricted to a narrow band in front of it having a width equal to the column length. Secondly, the wide side dispersion becomes vertical and so sound is directed upwards to the ceiling and upper walls where it produces unwanted reflections.

LISCA consists of one or two horizontal line-sources mounted in the ceiling, but its proportions and angle avoids the first drawback by making a virtue of it, and makes good use of the second.

The line-source in fact extends the whole width of the hall from side to side. There is thus no problem from end cut-off, because the whole audience area is within its frontal region of coverage. The end cut-off actually minimises reflections from the side walls, and so is an advantage.

The first line-source array is mounted a little forward from the first row of seats and just off the front edge of the platform, so it would be over the front aisle. The loudspeakers are not facing downward as with the ceiling matrix, but are tilted to an angle of 64° facing toward the audience.

59

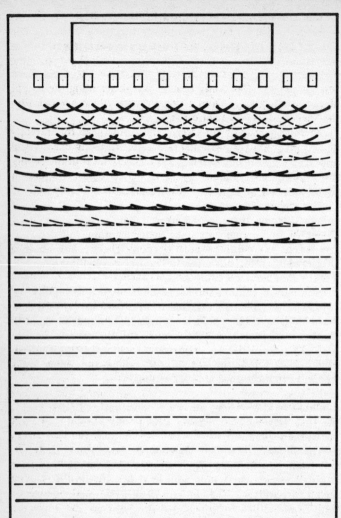

Fig. 17. LISCA sound pattern. The curved wave-fronts from each unit soon merge to form a plane or flat-fronted wave giving no cancellation effects and equal levels across the hall. Apparent sound source is the platform, and a pseudo stereo effect is often obtained. The most natural result of any system.

A sound pressure wave from a line-source begins as a series of spherical zones, but they quickly merge to form a single flat-fronted wave; this is known as a plane wave. Returning to our water analogy, instead of the circular ripples expanding out from several sources, the effect is more like a sea wave coming in on a flat sandy beach. It sweeps along the length of the auditorium as from a single source which acoustically, the line-source is (see Figure 17).

There can thus be no interference effects, so the intelligibility is accordingly high, and is consistent, being exactly the same at all points in the hall. Though mounted in the ceiling the angle of propagation avoids strongly exciting the vertical floor-to-ceiling resonance. The overall result is speech of exceptional clarity everywhere.

Feedback

The tilt of the loudspeakers of the first line-source array puts them sideways-on to the platform and the microphone. The angle is thus $90°$ and the output is $\cos 90°$ which is 0. Thus it is the region of zero propagation, and no direct sound at all can reach the microphone from them. This is in contrast to the ordinary ceiling matrix which, by facing downward, radiates sound from its first row back to the platform.

As with all systems, there can be feedback from reflected sound from the auditorium, but even this is reduced as there is little or no sound directed at the side walls.

Sound Levels and Range

Looking now at the theoretical sound levels obtaining, we will start at the first row which is almost beneath the first array. The significant dimension affecting all calculations, is the h, the height of the array above the seated audience head level which is about 3½ ft or 1 m. Thus h is the floor-to-ceiling height H, minus 3½ ft or 1 m. The first row is at an angle of $64°$ off-axis from the loudspeakers, which is the angle the line-source is tilted. The sound level there is therefore $\cos 64° = 0.44$ times that of the same distance along the on-axis line. This corresponds to an SPL of -7 dB.

The on-axis line converges with the audience head level at a distance from the array according to basic trigonometry of:

$h/\sin(90° - 64°) = h/0.44$ or $2.3\,h$. As the propagation loss from a line-source is 3 dB for a doubling of distance, the loss along the on-axis line to the point where it reaches the audience is about 3.5 dB.

So with a level of -7 dB under the array at the first row, and -3.5 dB at the on-axis point, the latter is 3.5 dB higher compared to the former and is the maximum level obtained over the range. Thus, using the first row as a reference level of 0 dB, the on-axis point is $+3.5$ dB.

This complies with the requirement set out in our first chapter, whereby the first rows should receive only enough amplified volume to reinforce the speaker's natural voice, and so should be lower than elsewhere.

As the distance from the audience in the first row to the speaker on the platform is likely to be less than between them and the overhead array, the Haas effect will make all the sound appear to come from the platform with little, if any, awareness of an overhead source. The effect is thus totally natural.

The floor distance from under the array to the $+3.5$ dB on-axis point is $h/\tan(90° - 64°) = h/0.49$, or approximately $2h$. So $2h$ is the floor distance from the first row to the on-axis point, over which the sound level increases to 3.5 dB.

Beyond this it declines as the line of propagation goes off-axis again and the distance increases. However, distance has less effect than may be expected. Remember that the SPL decreases with distance because of the expansion of the wave, spherically in the case of a doublet to give a loss of 6 dB per doubling of distance, and cylindrically with the line-source to drop 3 dB for a doubling of distance.

With LISCA, the wave expands cylindrically from the array until it fills the space between floor and ceiling and up to there obeys the normal attenuation law. But beyond this no further expansion is possible as it is constrained by the floor, ceiling and walls. So the effect is like sound travelling along a tube, and in theory there should be little further loss beyond this point.

There are though losses due to absorption by the audience, carpet (if fitted), curtains and padded seating. The range limit beyond $2h$ will thus depend on the furnishings. At $4h$ the propagation angle is narrowed to the point where the recessed loudspeaker cones begin to be masked by the ceiling. Low and mid frequencies are diffracted around the obstruction, but high frequencies are not, so intelligibility may start to deteriorate beyond this point. Also, the off-axis angle increasingly reduces the level. So $4h$ can be considered the maximum range to give adequate sound level with highest intelligibility. If the length of the hall from first row to last is greater than $4h$ a second line-source array will be necessary.

Many halls exceed this due to extra length, or low ceilings giving a low value for h, in which case a second line-source is necessary. This does not interfere with the first one if correctly located, and so there is no sacrifice of clarity and intelligibility.

The Second Line-source

The second line-source should be located, not where the output from the first is tailing off at $4h$, but where it is strongest at around $2h$ or a little beyond at $2\frac{1}{2}h$. Here, the output from the second array which is immediately overhead, is -3.5 dB compared to that from the first. So, with most of the sound coming from the first, the perceived location is still forward and there is virtually no awareness of the second array overhead.

Moving back from this point, the output from the first line-source starts to diminish while that from the second increases, thus maintaining an even sound level throughout. Furthermore, as the second array is now forward relative to the listener, the frontal natural source location is maintained.

In very long halls or those with a short h dimension, the distance from the proposed second line-source location to the last row of seats may exceed $4h$. In this case, the location of the second array may have to be taken back to $2\frac{1}{2}-3\ h$.

In this case there may then be some awareness of an overhead source immediately beneath it, as the output from the first is lower than $+3.5$ dB at this point. However, the effect would be local, and sound level and intelligibility would not be affected anywhere. The situation where the length of a hall from the first row of seats to the last would exceed $6h$ would be unusual.

It may be thought that having two arrays would create the interference comb-filter effects described in Chapter 4, that characterize the ceiling matrix. Two conditions are needed to produce these. First, the volume levels need to be similar, and second, the sound path difference between each source and the listener must be small. These conditions are satisfied in many places with the ceiling matrix, but nowhere with LISCA. Where the sound levels are similar, the path difference is large and vice-versa. So no interference problems are created by having two arrays.

Pseudo Stereo Effect

An unexpected effect was noticed with the prototype installation of LISCA. Not only did the sound come naturally from the front as it should, but it seemed to correspond to the location of speakers on the platform. When someone was speaking with a microphone to the right, the sound appeared to come from the front-right, and when from the left, the sound source seemed to correspond.

This was baffling at first, but the explanation seems to be as follows: Our ear/brain combination tries to identify the location of all sound we hear. It does this by comparing the phase of sounds received by the two ears. Those arriving at one ear before the other, are perceived to come from that direction; also the brain judges by the amount of phase difference the precise angle. This incidentally is why it is difficult to locate low frequency sounds, the wavelength is so long that there is virtually no phase difference from one ear to the other.

Nearby sounds are especially easy to locate because of their spherical wavefront, the curve ensuring that the sound to one ear is well in advance of the other. With more distant sounds, the curvature is much less, and so location is less easy.

With LISCA, the wavefront is plane, there is no curvature at all, and it arrives at both ears at precisely the same time. So there is no lateral directional information. The brain then seeks to replace the missing directional information with data from another sensor, the eyes. So, when observing participants at any position on the platform, the brain signals its auditory section that that is where the source is.

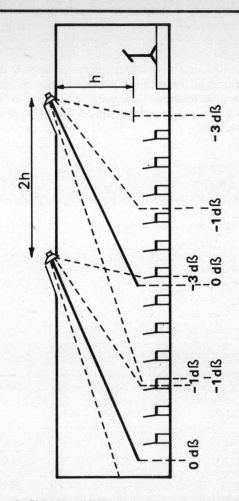

Fig. 18. Side view of LISCA double array, with sound pressure levels. The low level at the front is just sufficient to reinforce the direct sound from the platform. The −3dB level of the first array coincides with the 0dB level of the second. No point receives an equal level from both arrays, thus avoiding cancellation. This also maintains a forward source location at all points.

It is an illusion, but then so is stereo. Nonetheless, it results in an unexpected bonus of naturalness, which together with the desired graded sound level from the front, the even coverage over the rest of the auditorium, the extremely high degree of intelligibility and clarity, and the low feedback characteristic, surely makes LISCA the ultimate in public address loudspeaker systems.

Figure 18 shows a side view of LISCA double array with sound pressure levels.

Chapter 8

INSTALLING LISCA

The prototype installation consisted of several columns of triangular cross section, each containing a number of drive units. These were mounted horizontally at the required angle, end-to-end across the width of the hall, in a recess created in the suspended ceiling by removing the ceiling tiles. Deflector panels were fitted from the top edge of the columns sloping down to the next row of tiles. The recess was concealed by sheets of white expanded aluminium which replaced the removed tiles.

The visual effect was that the expanded aluminium blended in with the surrounding tiles and made the installation practically invisible. A lot of work was involved and a considerable amount of wood was needed for the columns and deflectors, this together with the sheets of expanded aluminium made it rather costly. However, in view of the excellent results obtained, it was judged well worth the effort and expenditure.

Since then though, a simpler and less costly way of achieving the same results has been devised, and this is the one we shall describe.

A line-source does not have to consist of a box with a row of loudspeakers inside. It can be made up of a row of individual units mounted separately. This will be found to be easier to implement, require less disturbance to the existing ceiling, and use cheaper materials and less of them.

Most modern halls have suspended tile ceilings and the installation here described has been designed for these. However, the principle of LISCA can be used with almost any ceiling although the mounting arrangements would have to be modified.

Planning

The first step is to survey the hall and determine exactly where the array is to be fitted. Also it will be necessary to determine whether a single line-source will be sufficient or two will be required.

As the dimension h, the ceiling-to-audience-head distance, is the vital one, this must be determined first. The floor-to-ceiling height must be measured, and 3½ ft or 1 metre subtracted to give distance h. It usually is between 6–8 ft for medium-sized halls.

The first array will be situated just off the edge of the platform and a little forward from the first row, so it will generally be over the front aisle. Measure from there back up the hall for a distance of 4 h; if this coincides with, or goes beyond the back row of seats, one line-source will be sufficient. If not, then a second one will be needed.

If the distance is greater than 6 h, the second line-source will have to be at 2½–3 h from the first. If it is 6 h or less, the location of the second will be at 2 h.

The rows of ceiling tiles nearest to these positions are the ones in which LISCA will be installed. It may be necessary to modify the location to an adjacent row to avoid light fittings, but this will not seriously affect the result.

The next stage is to determine how many individual units will be required. This depends on the number of tiles across the width of the hall. These are usually either 2 ft squares or 2 × 4 ft rectangles (or either 600 mm squares or 600 × 1,200 mm rectangles for metric tiles). In the case of the 2 ft square tiles, one unit will be needed for each tile, with the exception of the final ones adjacent to the walls. So if there are 16 tiles across the hall, 14 units will be required. Where two line-sources are needed, the number is obviously doubled.

If the rectangular tiles are fitted and they run lengthways across the hall width, two units are needed per tile, but the construction of the unit is the same as for the square. If rectangular tiles are arranged sideways to the width of the hall, the unit must be modified.

Unit Construction

The construction of the units is quite easy and straightforward. There are no angles to measure or to adjust when installed. The 64° angle is automatically obtained if the wood is cut to the given dimensions. The most difficult part is cutting the elliptical holes for the loudspeakers, but this is not too taxing if a power fretsaw is used. The hole does not have to be

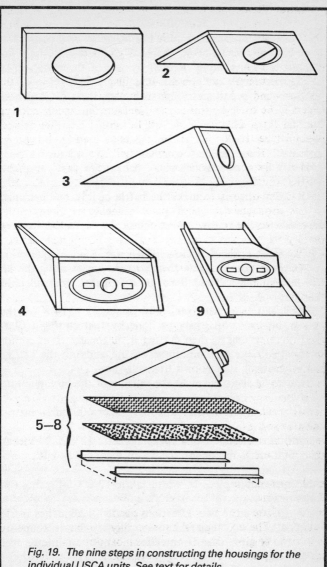

Fig. 19. The nine steps in constructing the housings for the individual LISCA units. See text for details.

perfect as it is not visible, see Figure 19.

The underneath is finished with inexpensive plasterer's expanded metal. As this is quite open the unit could be visible from beneath, so to avoid this and give a less conspicuous appearance, white fabric is used on top of the metal. The metal supports this and prevents it sagging.

Materials required are: Elliptical loudspeakers 7 × 4 inch or 6 × 4 inch; three-eighths plywood; T-section metal strip (as used for suspended ceilings); white muslin or other fabric; expanded metal (8ft × 2ft 3in sheets as used by plasterers, obtainable from builders merchants). Evo-stik wood glue; three-eighths screws; panel pins. Quantities depend on the number of units.

The first stage is to make the baffle boards, one per unit. This is a rectangular board 12 × 6 inches of three-eighths plywood. In the centre, cut an elliptical hole 3¼ × 6¼ inches for 7 × 4-inch units, or 3¼ × 5¼ for 6 × 4-inch drivers.

Second, cut the deflectors which are 12-inch squares of three-eighths ply, and glue them at right angles along the 12 inch side to the baffles. Two or three panel pins will hold them in place.

Third, cut two triangular wood pieces, 12 × 14 × 6⅜ths inches; this can most easily be done by first cutting a 12 × 6⅜ th inch rectangle, then cutting it diagonally from corner to corner. Glue and pin these to the ends of the baffle/deflector assembly, to form a triangular box.

Fourth, fit the speaker to the outside of the box, pointing inwards.

Fifth, cut two 2-ft lengths of T strip, or 600 mm if metric tiles are used.

Sixth, cut a section of expanded metal 12¾ × 24 inches (or × 600 mm). If cut the right way, eight can be cut from a 8ft × 2ft 3in sheet.

Seventh, cut a piece of white fabric 12¾ × 24 inches (or × 600 mm).

Eighth, place the two T sections parallel, 12¾ inches apart; and lay the expanded metal between them so that it is supported at the edges by the T-projections. Lay the fabric on top of the metal.

Ninth, place the box open side down, in the centre of the T

strips with its sides against the insides of the strips. Drill, and screw through the sides of the strips into the sides of the box, two screws per side. The units are now complete and ready to install.

Installation

First remove the ceiling tile and cut from it four pieces: two 24 × 5½ ins (or 600 × 135 mm if tiles are metric); and two 12¾ × 5 ins (324 × 122 mm for metric tiles). Fit the latter between the unit T strips fore and aft of the box pushing them well into the edge of the baffle and deflector boards to make a good air seal. These will also keep the fabric in place, but check that it hasn't rumpled in pressing the tile pieces home. Cut the 12¾ in or 324 mm dimension a little oversize so that the pieces will be a tight fit between the T strips. Experiment with the first one then cut the others accordingly.

The unit can then be slid into place in the centre of the empty tile space in the ceiling with the loudspeaker facing toward the audience. The remaining two tile pieces are fitted into the spaces on either side of the unit. Repeat for all the other units. The appearance is that of silver bands backed with white across the row of tiles, and is quite attractive.

These instructions are for square tiles. In the case of rectangular ones running lengthways across the width of the hall, the unit construction is exactly the same, but the fitting is different. Two units must be fitted per tile, so it needs four 12¾ × 5 in pieces to be cut from the tile to fit into the fore and aft positions. Three pieces are required as side fillers. Two are 24 × 5½ in pieces to go on either side of the two units; the third one is double this size, 24 × 11 ins (or 600 × 270 mm for metric tiles), which must be fitted in the middle. Thus the units are equally spaced from each other and adjacent ones.

For rectangular tiles running sideways across the hall width, twice as much T strip, expanded metal and fabric is required. The boxes are made as before, but they are mounted at the centre of two 4 ft T strips, and the fabric and expanded metal must also be 4 ft long, (1,200 mm for metric tiles). The fore and aft tile piece dimensions are: 12¾ × 17 ins (324 × 422 mm metric); and the side fillers 48 × 5½ ins (1,200 × 135

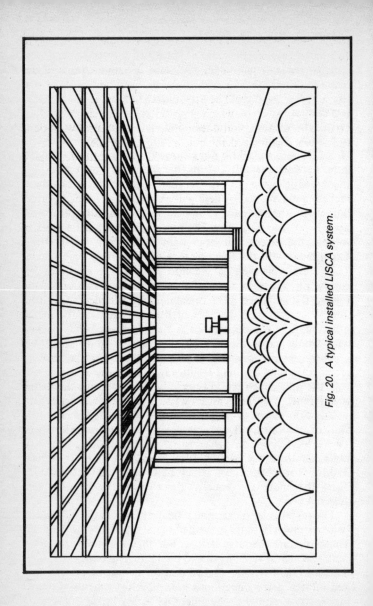

Fig. 20. A typical installed LISCA system.

mm). Being long and narrow, the side fillers will need care in cutting and handling.

In all cases, it will be an advantage to remove the adjacent row of tiles to help in manoeuvering the units and the side fillers into place. It will be essential when it comes to connecting the speakers, of which more in the next chapter. It is evident that installation does not involve structural alterations other than the removal and cutting of existing tiles.

A typical installed LISCA system is illustrated in Figure 20.

Chapter 9

LOW-IMPEDANCE MATCHING

It is a basic principle of electrical circuits that the maximum power is transferred from one to another when their respective impedances are the same. A high impedance circuit has a high voltage with low current whereas a low impedance circuit has low voltage and high current. It follows that if a low impedance circuit is connected to a high impedance source, the high voltage will drive an excessive current through the circuit with likely damage to the load or source or both. An analogy would be the connection of a 12V car lamp to the 240V mains supply, which would swiftly result in a blown lamp and a blown fuse. Not an experiment to be recommended!

On the other hand, connecting high impedance load across a low impedance source results in low current and low power transfer. Connecting a 240V mains lamp to a car battery would not even produce a glimmer.

So, for maximum power transfer, the output impedance of the amplifier should equal that of the loudspeaker system, although as we shall see, maximum power transfer is not always the sole consideration with public address systems.

In all cases though, the loudspeaker impedance must be equal or greater than that of the amplifier, never less. A lower impedance would draw high current from the amplifier output transistors causing overload distortion to start at a lower power level, and excessive heat which could destroy bipolar transistors.

Low-impedance Circuits

Ordinary domestic amplifiers which are often used for small public address systems have a low impedance output of 4–8 Ω. Public address amplifiers have a range of low impedances, usually 4, 8, and 16 Ω and in addition high impedance output on the 70V and/or 100V lines.

In accord with the rule stated above, impedances of the loudspeaker system must always total more than 4 Ω. There may though be other loads such as an inductive hearing aid loop which are also connected to the amplifier. As the total load impedance must be higher than 4 Ω, the loudspeaker circuit must therefore be much higher where such additional loads are connected.

When two load circuits are connected to the same source, the power fed to each is equal if the impedances are equal. If they are not, most power will go to the lower impedance load. An induction loop usually requires more power than the loudspeakers, so it must be of lower impedance than the loudspeaker system. This means that the loudspeakers must be much higher in impedance.

A typical example is for the induction loop to be 7 Ω. To achieve a total above 4 Ω, the loudspeaker system must be 12 Ω. This gives just about the correct power division, although we shall see more about this in a later chapter.

To calculate two impedances in parallel there are two methods:

$$Z = \frac{z_1 \times z_2}{z_1 + z_2}$$

or

$$\frac{1}{Z} = \frac{1}{z_1} + \frac{1}{z_2} .$$

The former is the easiest as the latter involves reciprocals, although these are easy if you have a calculator that does them. For more than two impedances the latter must be used, adding further reciprocals for the extra impedances. Using either of these for our example of 7 Ω and 12 Ω gives 4.4 Ω.

For impedances in series we just add them together.

The standard loudspeaker impedance is 8 Ω, but 4 Ω units can be obtained and also 16 Ω. Sometimes the latter are advertised at low cost in the electronics magazines and considerable savings can be made by using them. Impedances can be adjusted to those required by a series/parallel arrangement.

76

Series-parallel Connection

Almost any number of loudspeaker units of any impedance can be brought to the required value by appropriate series-parallel connection. One useful rule of thumb is that an x number of parallel groups each consisting of x number units in series, will give the same impedance as a single unit. For example, five 8 Ω units in series gives an impedance of 40 Ω; and five such groups in parallel gives an impedance of 8 Ω, the same as the single loudspeaker. This works for any number providing the number of groups is the same as the number of units in each group.

Different impedances can be obtained by varying either the number of groups or the number in each group. However, to obtain equal power from all units, the number in each group must be the same.

For example, groups of six units give impedances of 48 Ω each. Parallel four groups to obtain 12 Ω, see Figure 21. However, if we divided up those 24 loudspeakers into six groups of four, each group would have an impedance of 32 Ω, and six in parallel would give 5.3 Ω. The former would be required if an induction loop was also being operated, but the latter would be satisfactory if there was no other load.

In many cases the total impedance is greater than that of the amplifier, and so maximum power transfer is not achieved. This does not mean that power is wasted, it is just not fully developed in the amplifier. Maximum power transfer is not the sole consideration for small and medium sized installations. A hall seating 200 probably requires less than 10 watts fed to the loudspeakers, whereas most modern amplifiers are rated at 40–100 watts, so there is usually plenty to spare. The total load impedance can thus be well above that rated for the amplifier.

There is an advantage in this, because amplifier distortion usually decreases as the load impedance increases, also the output stage will run cooler, which improves its reliability factor.

The impedance can be too high though, in which case the amplifier will provide insufficient power to drive it. Volume controls and mixer faders then have to be set toward maximum, which could overload the later amplifier stages on strong

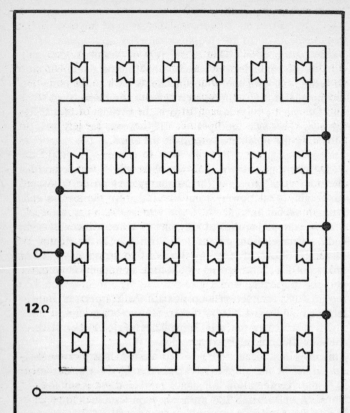

Fig. 21. A series-parallel circuit of 24 units arranged in four groups of six. Impedance is 12Ω for 8Ω units.

input signals, so producing distortion.

This is more likely to happen with lower-powered amplifiers, but the answer is to prevent it by keeping the load impedance within reasonable limits. As a rough guide, around 5 times could be considered to be the maximum, while a good minimum could be 1¼ times. It can of course go lower than this, down to the actual amplifier impedance if necessary. The ideal range is thus 1¼–5 times amplifier impedance. The connecting wiring is likely to add about an ohm, so this gives a safety margin if the load impedance is close to that of the amplifier.

Most LISCA installations need two arrays and it is convenient though not essential, if each can be a complete and separate circuit with its individual cable back to the amplifier. Then either can be run separately from the other for testing. The number of units in each array is the number of tiles across the hall minus two, as those nearest the walls are left free. In most cases the units will range from 12 to 16.

As there is more than one way to connect an array, the choice depends on the impedance required which in turn depends on whether one or two arrays are to be used, and whether an induction loop is to be run from the same amplifier. We will look at the different numbers of units in a single array in turn to see what arrangements are possible with each.

12 — Two groups of six 8 Ω units give an impedance of 24 Ω, [2 @ 6 $\times$ 8 Ω = 24 Ω]. For two arrays this is 12 Ω and is ideal for installations that include an induction loop, for optimum matching.

A 12-unit array can also consist of three groups of four to give 10.6 Ω [3 @ 4 $\times$ 8 Ω = 10.6 Ω] or four groups of three which produces 6 Ω [4 @ 3 $\times$ 8 Ω = 6 Ω]. Either of these could be used for single arrays.

It may be desired to use 16 Ω units which are often available at low cost. In this case the three by four arrangement [3 @ 4 $\times$ 16 Ω = 21.3 Ω] gives 21.3 Ω, which is suitable for a double array installation resulting in a combined impedance of 10.6 Ω. With a 7 Ω loop this gives a total of 4.2 Ω.

For a double array without a loop, the four by three [4 @ 3 $\times$ 16 Ω = 12 Ω] gives 12 Ω each hence, 6 Ω for the two.

13 — Thirteen units cannot be divided into equal groups, so resistive padding must be resorted to. One group consists of seven and the other of six units, with a 4 or 5 Ω 5-watt resistor being included to pad the value of the 6-unit group [1 @ 7, 1 @ 6+r $\times$ 8 Ω = 28 Ω]. Two arrays thus give an impedance of 14 Ω. The use of 16 Ω units in this case would give a rather high impedance of 56 Ω for a single or 28 Ω for a double array. However, if an 8 Ω amplifier tap is available,

this could be used to give a closer match, or better still, a 16 Ω tap.

If a loop is installed, this can be fed from the 4 Ω tap while the loudspeakers are supplied from the 8 or 16 Ω. In doing this care must be taken to ensure that the total load as seen by the amplifier does not exceed its rating. So for example, if a loop of 8 Ω was connected to the 4 Ω tap, it would half load the amplifier. An additional 32 Ω load connected to the 16 Ω tap would also half load the amplifier, so fully loading it. Therefore 32 Ω is the minimum limit for the second load.

So to determine whether the amplifier would be overloaded in any particular case, express the amplifier tap impedance over the load connected to it, as a fraction, and do the same with the second load, then add the two fractions. If the result is greater than unity the amplifier will be overloaded, if less, the loads are within the rating. This can be done also with a third load and tap such as for auxiliary loudspeakers.

14 − The obvious option with fourteen units is two groups of seven which result in 28 Ω for a single array [2 @ 7 × 8 Ω = 28 Ω], and 14 Ω for a double. As with the 13-unit array, 16 Ω units could be used if a higher amplifier tap is available.

If not, they still could be used by having seven groups of two [7 @ 2 × 16 Ω = 4.6 Ω] for a single array and no other load. A double array could be achieved by connecting them in series to give 9.2 Ω. An 8 Ω loop could be used with this, but that is the lowest resistance value that could be tolerated. As most of the power should go to the loop, a 9.2/8 ratio is not sufficient and the loop most likely would be underpowered.

15 − Three groups of five [3 @ 5 × 8 Ω = 13.3 Ω] is a good configuration for a single array. For a double, the impedance is 6.6 Ω which is satisfactory, but does not allow for a loop. Here, 16 Ω units could be used to advantage [3 @ 5 × 16 Ω = 26.6 Ω], giving 13.3 for the double array.

An alternative is five groups of three [5 @ 3 × 16 Ω = 9.6 Ω] using 16 Ω units, with two arrays giving 4.8 Ω. This could be used if there is no other load. A series connection of arrays would give 19.2 Ω which could be useful if the loop is low in value or there are auxiliary loudspeakers.

16 − A two group of eight system [2 @ 8 × 8 Ω = 32 Ω] is the most practical arrangement for a sixteen-unit array when

two arrays are needed as well as a loop. The resulting impedance is 16 Ω for both arrays.

Using 16 units [2 @ 8 × 16 Ω = 64 Ω] produces 32 Ω for a double array, which is rather too high unless a higher amplifier tap is used. A twin four system [4 @ 4 × 16 Ω = 16 Ω] gives a satisfactory 8 Ω for two arrays, but this is too low to operate a loop as well.

It can thus be seen that there are many possibilities for getting the right impedance and that the choice depends on whether one or two arrays are required, and also the extra loading of a loop. Great care must be exercised to observe polarity. Within a group, units are connected from positive to negative; when paralleling groups all positives go together.

Auxiliary Loudspeakers

Most installations require the fitting of one or more extra loudspeakers running at low level in mother's rooms, ante rooms and the like. Usually there is ample power to supply these, but they can result in matching problems.

Connecting an 8 Ω loudspeaker directly across the amplifier 4 Ω output would half load it and so feed it with more power than the auditorium arrays. The most satisfactory method is to run it through a transformer from the amplifier 100V line output, but more of this later. If the amplifier is not a dedicated p.a. amplifier, it probably will not have a 100V line facility.

If there is an output transformer offering a range of low-impedance tappings, there is a trick method not generally known, whereby a very low output impedance can be obtained to run one or two low level loudspeakers. It consists of taking an output from *between* two of the regular tappings.

The transformer secondary starts at a common terminal to which is connected one end of the winding. The first tap is the 4 Ω, then the 8 Ω and finally the winding ends with the 16 Ω terminal. It may be thought that an output taken between 4 Ω and 8 Ω would be the difference between them, that is 4 Ω, and likewise one taken between 8 Ω and 16 Ω would be 8 Ω. This is not so, the windings progress in a non-linear manner, the turns ratio depending on the square root of the impedance.

81

To find the impedance between two regular tappings, the following formula can be used:

$$Z_0 = (\sqrt{Z_1} - \sqrt{Z_2})^2$$

in which Z_0 is the impedance between tappings; Z_1 the higher impedance tapping; and Z_2 the lower impedance.

This produces some rather surprising and interesting results. Between the 4 Ω and 8 Ω tappings, the impedance is 0.68 Ω, while between the 8 Ω and the 16 Ω ones, the impedance is 1.37 Ω.

An 8 Ω auxiliary loudspeaker can be run from the 0.68 Ω impedance and will load the amplifier to only 0.085 of its capacity, see Figure 22. This is equivalent to a 47 Ω load across the 4 Ω tapping and can be reckoned as such in calculating the total impedance as previously described.

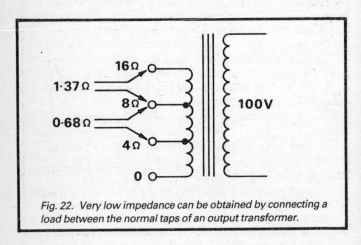

Fig. 22. Very low impedance can be obtained by connecting a load between the normal taps of an output transformer.

If the amplifier does not have various output tappings it can be assumed to have a 4 Ω output, and a small 100V line transformer can be used to run up to two auxiliaries. Ignore the primary that is tapped in watts, and connect the 0–8 Ω tappings to the amplifier, the auxiliary loudspeaker can then be connected across the 8–16 Ω tappings.

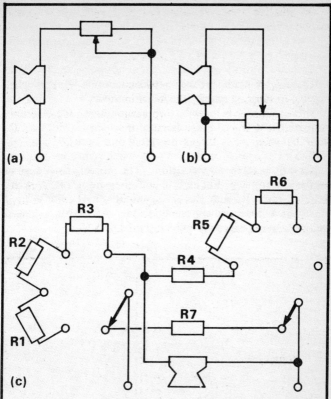

Fig. 23. Volume controls for auxiliary loudspeakers. (a) simple series variable resistor; (b) the resistor is connected as potentiometer to maintain a load on the amplifier; (c) a switched control which maintains the same load on the amplifier at all settings (see text for resistor values).

An alternative method of running an auxiliary loudspeaker is to use a 16 Ω unit, and connect a 5-watt 25 Ω resistor in series with it. This gives a loading of 41 Ω, but gives a lower volume from the speaker than the transformer method as over half the power fed to it is dissipated in the resistor. In either case a switch can be incorporated in series to switch it off as required.

One or two low-level speakers can be switched off or on without affecting the others, but if a large number are installed, some means of maintaining the same load on the line is necessary.

Volume controls can also be fitted, although for low level units these are hardly necessary. These can be a simple series variable resistor, a potentiometer to provide a load for the amplifier when it is turned down and minimise the effect on other units, or a matching attenuator which provides a constant load at all positions, as illustrated by Figure 23.

The latter uses a 2-pole five way switch giving one full, one off, and three attenuated positions. The resistor values depend on the loudspeaker. For an 8 Ω unit, they are R1, R2, R4 and R5 2 Ω each; R3 and R6, 4 Ω; and R7, 8 Ω. For a 16 Ω loudspeaker these values are doubled. All resistors should be 2 watt rating except R7 which should be 5 watt.

Chapter 10

100V LINE SYSTEMS

All dedicated public-address amplifiers have in addition to the usual low-impedance output terminals, one labelled '100V line'; some have also a 70V output. These are often a puzzle to the uninitiated. Why are they rated in volts instead of ohms? How in fact can a voltage be specified when the signal is constantly varying? These are questions often asked. Furthermore, why should anything other than the low-impedance outputs be used anyway?

We will take the last question first. In a large installation, cable runs of several hundred yards or metres may be involved. With twin 13/0.2 cable having a resistance of 9 Ω per 100 m, it can be seen that by operating a single low impedance loudspeaker of 8 Ω on the end of a 100 m run, over half of the power is dissipated in the cable. If another unit is spurred off, the impedance drops to 4 Ω and even greater loss takes place. It may not be practical to series the units as it may be required to switch them.

This situation where several loudspeakers are needed at the end of a long cable run is a common one, and is quite impractical with low-impedance operation. The answer is run them at high impedance. Then the resistance of the cable is small compared to the loudspeaker impedance. At an impedance of 2,000 Ω for example, the 9 Ω of a 100 m cable run is insignificant. The impedance is converted down to that of the individual loudspeaker unit by means of a transformer.

Why Voltage?

It is of course true that the output voltage from the amplifier is constantly varying with the signal. The 100V is obtained when the amplifier is delivering its maximum rated sine wave output; likewise with the 70V output. If the voltage is thus fixed, the actual output impedance depends on the wattage rating of the amplifier. So for a 50-watt amplifier, the impedance is: $Z = E^2/W = 10,000/50 = 200$ Ω. A 100-watt amplifier has an impedance of $10,000/100 = 100$ Ω.

At first sight this may seem an unnecessarily involved way of specifying an output impedance. It may be thought better to have a standard output impedance such as 200 Ω and stick to it irrespective of the power rating of the amplifier, just as is done with the low impedance outputs.

The reason is that it makes it more convenient to calculate the power and loading when using a number of loudspeakers of mixed power ratings.

The loudspeaker transformers have tapped primaries and secondaries. In the case of the secondaries, these are tapped at the low impedances of 4 Ω and 8 Ω for appropriate connection to the loudspeaker. The primaries are tapped at various wattage ratings and thereby the loudspeaker receives whatever power is designated by the chosen tapping.

As it is the primary that is so tapped, the maximum number of turns are in circuit at the lowest power rating. The highest power is given by the fewest number of turns, hence the lowest tap, see Figure 24.

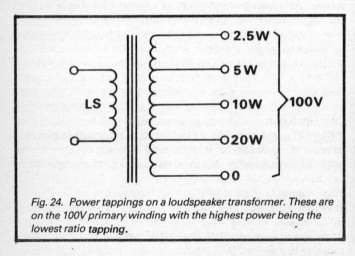

Fig. 24. *Power tappings on a loudspeaker transformer. These are on the 100V primary winding with the highest power being the lowest ratio* tapping. ·

The system is somewhat analogous to the electricity supply mains where there is a fixed voltage and appliances of different wattage ratings connected. We do not concern ourselves with the impedance of the appliances, or that of the mains supply, only the wattage rating and whether the mains feed can supply it.

Calculation of Load

To determine whether the load is within the capability of the amplifier to supply, all that is necessary is to add up the various wattage ratings to which the individual loudspeakers in the system are tapped, and ensure that the total is less than the power rating of the amplifier. If it exceeds it, then some units will have to be tapped down to a lower rating until the figures tally.

Although the output impedance of an amplifier at 100V differs for different amplifier power ratings, this is of no concern. A 100V line transformer will produce its specified power from any amplifier.

The system is much more convenient than calculating the total impedance to ensure that it is greater than that of the amplifier, which would be quite a chore with a large installation. Also, widely varying sound levels can be obtained from the same feeder by simply adjusting the transformer taps. This is especially useful in factories, where high volumes may be required in the machine shop, but much lower ones elsewhere. Likewise in a large auditorium, high power levels are required there while moderate ones only are needed in rest rooms.

70V Operation

While the wattage ratings are thus used as a convenience, really of course, it is the impedance of the loads that are being adjusted in disguise to match or exceed that of the amplifier, just as with the low-impedance circuits.

We have seen that the output impedance of a 50-watt amplifier is 200 Ω. If now we perform the same calculation at 70V, we get: $Z = E^2/W = 4900/50 = 98\ \Omega$. So the output impedance of an amplifier at its 70V tapping is almost half as much as it is at the 100V output.

This means that twice as many loudspeakers of the same impedance can be connected before their impedance drops below that of the amplifier, although only half the rated power of the transformer tapping will be available from each.

The 70V output is therefore useful if a large number of loudspeakers are required to operate at low volume, and their combined watts exceed the power rating of the amplifier.

Transformers

100V transformers are available for a wide range of maximum powers from around 4 watts to 40 watts. Each usually has three or four lower tappings. For example one 4-watt transformer has tappings at 2, 1, and ½-watt. A 40-watt model has them at 30, 20, and 10 watts. For general public-address work a 15-watt transformer with taps at 10, 5, 2½, and 1¼ watts is very useful as it will drive anything from a large column to a subdued mother's room loudspeaker.

There is less choice of impedance with the secondaries, being usually 8 Ω, tapped at 4 Ω. Higher impedances can though be accommodated just as when connected to the low impedance amplifier output. The power is then proportionally less. So, a 16 Ω load can be connected to the 8 Ω terminal and the power rating halved. This is useful in the case of columns which, having a series or series/parallel connection of drivers, are usually of higher impedance.

Unlike the amplifier low impedance output, loudspeaker impedances can also be taken below the rated impedance of the transformer secondary, in this case the power rating is proportionately increased. So, a column with predominantly parallel connected units to achieve tapering (see Fig. 12), resulting in an impedance of 2 Ω, could be connected to the 4 Ω tap. The power rating would then be double that indicated on the primary wattage tapping.

In all such cases of modification of the secondary impedance, it is the actual power ratings which thereby results, and not that indicated on the transformer primary terminals, that must be totted up to determine the power taken from the amplifier.

If a transformer is required for an unusual load impedance that cannot be accommodated in the above manner, the turns ratio TR can be calculated from:

$$TR = \frac{E}{\sqrt{(Z \times W)}}$$

It is worthy of note that while care should be taken with all loudspeaker systems to avoid short-circuits, especial care is needed with 100V line systems. With low impedance, a short at the loudspeaker end puts the resistance of the cable across the amplifier, this is probably a couple of ohms across the 4 Ω output. It thus may not cause immediate and catastrophic damage if the signal level is not high and the short is soon removed.

With a 100V line system, a short places a couple of ohms across an output impedance of 100 Ω in the case of 100-watt amplifier. The result will almost certainly be the destruction of the amplifier output transistors unless it has short-circuit protection.

LISCA Distribution

In the case of LISCA arrays and for conventional columns in medium-sized halls, 100V operation is unnecessary. The units can be series-paralleled to obtain a suitable impedance as shown in the last chapter. Cable resistance is only a small fraction of the total load impedance, so although there is some power loss it is quite small. All units are operated at the same power level so the transformer tappings offer no advantage. The cost of providing a transformer for each unit in a LISCA array would also be high. The 100V system is most effective for large installations, especially where there are a number of individual loudspeakers that may be required to run at different volume levels.

One installation was encountered where the units of a ceiling matrix system were all connected in series and fed from the 100V line output. In theory this should have been quite satisfactory as the total impedance of the loudspeakers was around 200 Ω and the power rating of the amplifier was 50 watts, which gives a 200 Ω output impedance at 100V.

However, a short-circuit did appear on the cable resulting in the instant demise of the amplifier. Even without this hazard, there was another. While loudspeakers rarely go open-circuit, they sometimes do. Usually this is due to a dry joint on the connection between the coil and the flexible lead-out wire. But whatever the cause, if all the loudspeakers are in series, one open-circuit results in all going silent, and it is then a major job finding the culprit.

In a series-parallel arrangement, an open-circuit only affects one group, so there is only a partial loss of sound. Furthermore the fault is narrowed down to the affected group and so easier to trace. This instance then is an example of that which is theoretically possible is not always practically advisable.

Mixed Operation

In many cases it is convenient to have part of the installation such as the LISCA system in the auditorium, running at low impedance, while other parts including loudspeakers in ante rooms operate from the 100V output. This is an alternative to the method described in the last chapter of running such auxiliaries from between the 4 Ω and 8 Ω output tappings to achieve very low impedance.

The disadvantage is that a transformer is needed for each loudspeaker, but the advantage is that a larger number can be operated and each adjusted to the required individual sound level. With the inter-tapping method, more than two loudspeakers would impose a load that was an appreciable proportion of the total load on the amplifier. (Three 8 Ω loudspeakers so connected would comprise a quarter of the load.)

When operating a dual system care must be taken that the total load of both sections do not exceed the amplifier rating. To ensure this, firstly determine how much the amplifier is loaded by the main system which is the auditorium low-impedance circuit. Let us say for example, the total low-impedance load including loudspeaker system and induction loop is 5 Ω which is connected across the 4 Ω output. This means that the amplifier is running at four-fifths of its load capacity, which leaves one-fifth available for auxiliary circuits.

Translating this into power, if the amplifier is rated at 50 watts, then one-fifth or 10 watts maximum are available. So, all the transformer tappings of the auxiliary loudspeakers must add up to less than 10 watts. This would then fully load the amplifier, but as mentioned earlier it is prudent to under-run it if possible, so a lower figure should be aimed at.

It can be seen from this that the loading can be quite tight, which is why it is an advantage to arrange the main loudspeaker and loop circuits to give a good margin by keeping their combined impedance well above 5 Ω if possible.

Adding a Transformer

It may be necessary to feed several individual loudspeakers in various ante rooms from an amplifier that has no 100V output or output transformer with tappings between which a very low-impedance output can be obtained. In such case a 100V line transformer can be installed at the amplifier to convert it to partial 100V line working.

The turns ratio required can be calculated from the same formula as for a loudspeaker transformer:

$$TR = \frac{E}{\sqrt{(Z \times W)}}$$

but in this case Z is the output impedance of the amplifier which in most cases will be 4 Ω, and W is its rated output.

Ratios for popular amplifier powers are from this: 40w, 7.9; 50w, 7.0; 75w, 5.8; and 100w, 5.0.

It may be possible to obtain transformers designed for these powers from specialist firms, or some transformer winding firms will make one to order although this can be rather expensive.

An alternative is to use a small mains transformer having the same ratios. The low-voltage secondary should be connected to the amplifier output and the 240V mains primary to the 100V loudspeaker circuit.

Some mains transformers having the same or near ratios to those required for the popular amplifier powers mentioned above are: 40w, 30V; 50w, 35V; 75w, 40V; and 100w, 48V. The voltages in these descriptions are those of the transformer secondary connected to the amplifier. Any other secondaries can be ignored.

The transformer current rating can be quite low. It is unlikely that more than 10 watts would be required for the auxiliary loudspeakers, so 250mA, which gives 10VA at 40V should suffice.

Chapter 11

TRANSMISSION LINES

The need to install very large loudspeaker distribution systems in which the cable is measured in thousands rather than hundreds of metres is comparatively rare. Domestic relay systems or large factory complexes are examples. We will then deal briefly with the principles involved in this chapter so that the reader will have some idea how to handle such a project should it arise.

With small and medium sized installations, the main consideration is that of the resistance of the loudspeaker cables. As we saw in the last chapter, its effect can be reduced by operating at high impedance by means of the 100V line.

In the case of very long cables there are other characteristics to be considered. These are four: resistance, inductance, capacitance and conductance. Resistance we are familiar with. Inductance we may think of only in connection with coils and windings, but all conductors, even a straight piece of wire, possess inductance.

When a current flows, a circular magnetic field is set up around the conductor, and as the current fluctuates, so does the field. The lines of force start from within the conductor and cut through its outer layers thereby inducing a back emf in them. Thus the conductor exhibits the property of inductance.

For a straight wire, the inductance is very small, and at audio frequencies and for moderate lengths has little effect. However, like resistance it is proportional to length, so with very long conductors it becomes significant. Also like resistance, it is in series with the circuit. The unit is the *henry*.

Capacitance is the third characteristic. The two conductors of a loudspeaker feeder are in close proximity, hence they possess the property of capacitance. The amount depends on the distance between the conductors, which in turn depends on the thickness of the insulating material, and the area of the conductor that is facing the other. This area is governed by the size of the conductor, and the length of the cable. The unit is the *farad* though it is usually expressed in sub multiples, and the capacitance is in parallel.

The fourth factor is conductance. Although we commonly speak of insulators as though they completely blocked the passage of an electric current this is not so. The perfect insulator has not yet been discovered if in fact it exists. All conduct to a certain degree.

Conduction through cable insulation is very small, and for normal lengths can be ignored, but for extremely long runs, it does have an effect. As with the other characteristics, it is proportional to length. The unit was the *mho*. This is ohm spelt backwards, and as conductance is the reciprocal of resistence, it is a very appropriate term. However, as with so many others, it has been changed by the unimaginative authorities who delight in changing everything for the sake of it, to the undescriptive term *siemens*. Fortunately, unlike some other terms that have been changed and given different values and require mental arithmetic to convert them, they have left the value of this one alone so that 1 mho = 1 siemen.

So then, the cable, which for very long lengths is termed a transmission line, has an impedance that is dependant on these four factors. The equivalent circuit is shown by Figure 25 and the formula is:

$$Z = \sqrt{\frac{(R + 2\pi fL)}{(G + 2\pi fC)}}$$

where Z is the impedance in ohms; R is the resistance in ohms; f is the frequency in Hz; L the inductance in henries; G the conductance in mhos; and C is the capacitance in farads. The impedance is known as its characteristic impedance and is not dependant on length.

Recalling the principle that maximum power is transferred from one circuit to another only if their impedances match, then the input circuit must be matched to the line at the start, and the line must be matched to the loudspeakers at the end.

The snag is that as frequency is included in the formula, the impedance holds good for only one frequency. At all others there will be a mis-match and loss of power. This

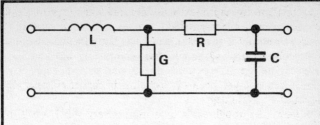

Fig. 25. The equivalent circuit of a transmission line containing inductance, conductance, resistance and capacitance.

means frequency distortion, the emphasis of one frequency at which optimum power transfer takes place above all others.

On examination of the formula it can be seen that if L/R is equal to C/G, then the effect of frequency on the top part of the equation will be equal to that on the bottom. Its effect is thus cancelled, and frequency no longer affects the result. Matching is thereby constant over the whole frequency range, and the line is said to be distortionless, behaving as a pure resistance.

Unfortunately, the four values do not balance up with practical cables as the inductance is too low, but this can be overcome by adding inductance in the form of a small coil in series with the line. The value can be calculated from the formula:

$$L = \frac{C \ R}{G}$$

This is termed lump-loading, because all the inductance is lumped into a single position. Coil insertion causes an abrupt change of impedance and a reflected wave is sent back to the source, causing loss of power and distortion. It is in fact better to divide the line up into several sections each with a loading coil, rather than load it at one go.

The best method is to continuously load the line by increasing its inductance along its whole length. One method of doing this is to wind iron wire around the conductors, but it is also expensive. A lump loaded line has more distortion than one continuously loaded but much less than an unloaded one of the same length.

Chapter 12

HEARING-AID INDUCTION LOOPS

When sound from a public-address system is picked up with a hearing-aid, it sounds indistinct, boxy and distant. This is partly due to it being heard with only one ear, as hearing normally with two ears subjectively compensates for hall reverberation. Also, nearby sounds such as coughs, whispers, programme rustling, and babies crying, sound much louder in proportion, when heard through a hearing-aid. To overcome these problems an increasing number of halls of all sizes are providing induction loops.

When receiving the programme from a loop, the result is as if the earpiece is connected directly to the speaker's microphone. The sound is loud and clear, hall acoustics are minimised, and extraneous noises are not heard at all. There is no need for special seating areas, the programme can be picked up anywhere in the hall, and often in adjacent ante-rooms as well. There is no doubt that the induction loop is the biggest boon to those with hearing defects since the production of the modern hearing-aid itself and should be fitted to every hall.

It is a fairly straightforward installation to make, as it consists of simply running a loop of cable around the perimeter of the hall and connecting it to the amplifier, but there are factors to be considered. These are: the gauge of the cable, the number of turns in the loop, its position, matching its resistance along with other loads to that of the amplifier, and the power available from the amplifier.

First of all, it must be noted that the signal is picked up by hearing-aids that have a two-position switch. One position is marked M, and is the normal one that has the internal microphone connected. The other is marked T, which introduces a small coil into the circuit. Originally, this was intended to pick up magnetic fields from telephone handsets, thereby giving a clearer result when using the telephone. All NHS hearing-aids made since 1974 have this switch, but many private models do not. These are the ones that fit totally inside the ear and so do not have room for a coil and switch.

Field Strength

The ideal strength is that which presents a signal to the hearing-aid which is comparable to the output of the internal microphone. Too weak a signal is not desirable as this means the user has to turn up the gain of the hearing-aid thereby making the noise of the internal amplifier noticeable. The British Standard BS.6083 Part 4: 1981 specifies the optimum strength as 100 mA in a single-turn loop of 1 metre diameter.

This reveals a basic factor that it is the current and the number of turns that influence the resulting field in any given size of loop, not voltage. Negligible power is extracted from the loop by the hearing-aids, so the voltage required is only that needed to drive the current through the loop. If the resistance can be made very low, the necessary current can be achieved with only a small voltage. However, as the magnetic field is proportional to the product of the current and the number of turns, it can be an advantage to increase the number of turns even though this also increases the resistance as we shall see later. Resistance can be reduced if necessary by using a heavier gauge cable.

The specified current of 100 mA/metre diameter is for an average signal level, but peaks will exceed this by several times. The British Standard recommends allowing for peaks of 12 dB above average which increases the current requirement by four times. If dynamic range compression is used in the amplifier, this can be reduced.

When the signal is to be mainly that of speech, a lesser allowance for peaks should be adequate. In practice, an allowance of 6 dB or twice the average has been found to be sufficient, but to provide a reasonable margin, the calculations that follow assume peaks of 10 dB which is three times the average.

If then the required average current is 0.1 amps per metre loop diameter d, the current in amps is $d/10$ and the peak current $3d/10$ amps.

This is the case for a circular loop, but as few halls apart from the famous London home of the Proms are circular, the amount needs to be modified. A square loop needs slightly more current to provide the same field, about 112 mA for a square having sides of 1 metre. The formula thereby becomes: $3d/9$ amps.

Taking it a stage further, few halls are square, most being rectangular. To find the exact figure for the current is rather complicated, but for practical purposes, we can arrive at a close figure for halls that have a length that is no more than 1½ times the width. We find the area by multiplying length by width, then take the square root. Hence the formula is: $3\sqrt{(1w)}/9$, where l and w are the length and width in metres, or to simplify it: $\sqrt{(a)}/3$, where a is the area.

In the case of long narrow areas things are rather different. With a square loop, each side contributes equally to the field, but if a small square section somewhere near the middle of a long narrow loop is considered, the short sides are too far away to have much effect, and only the central parts of the long sides are generating field within the section. Hence the field is approximately half what it would be for a square loop of the same width. At the ends of the rectangle three sides are contributing, so the field is about three-quarters of a similar square. Field strength thus varies over the length, being greatest at the ends, see Figure 26.

Turns

So far we have considered only single-turn loops. These in practice are not very efficient, requiring large currents to produce the required magnetic field and also creating amplifier matching difficulties because of having so low a resistance. The current needed is reduced in proportion to the number of turns, so our formula becomes $\sqrt{(a)}/3t$, in which t is the number of turns.

It may seem that running a cable several times around a hall would not only be somewhat of a chore, but result in a rather unsightly bunch of cables. There is a very practical way of avoiding this, that is by using a single run of three-core mains cable, or if the resistance value requires it, two twin-core cables. The cores are connected in series thereby producing a loop of three turns or four turns respectively.

Cables and Resistance

The type of cable used is governed mainly by the resistance required to match the amplifier output impedance, and the length of the run. The first thing to do then, is to measure up

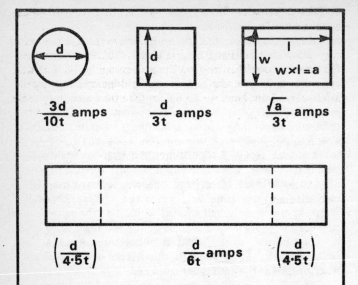

Fig. 26. Induction loop currents required for circular, square and rectangular loops. With the long rectangle, the currents shown produce the necessary fields in the areas indicated. As the current must be the same in all parts of the loop, the larger current for the central region is the one required.

the perimeter including any deviations such as alcoves and doorframes.

Next, determine the resistance that would best match with the amplifier. If two amplifiers are being used, one for the loudspeaker system and the other for the loop, the resistance can be from 5–8 Ω to match the 4 Ω output of the amplifier. If it is to be run from the same amplifier as the loudspeakers, it should be around 7–8 Ω, in which case the loudspeaker system would need to be about 12 Ω or more.

With a single amplifier, the output from the loop is governed by the feedback point of the main p.a. system, even though there is no feedback from the magnetic field of the loop. The reason is because the volume level obtainable from the loudspeakers is controlled by the feedback level. As the loop is connected across the loudspeaker system, its output too must be influenced by feedback.

Because the power fed to the loudspeakers is not usually very great, matters must be arranged so that more power is fed into the loop than the loudspeaker system, if the required current is to be produced. This can be done by designing the loudspeaker impedance to be higher than the resistance of the loop.

CABLE RESISTANCE TABLE

Cores No/Dia (mm)	Area (mm^2)	Current (A)	Resistance (per 100m)
1/0.2	–	–	57.6
7/0.2	0.22	1.4	8.2
13/0.2	0.4	2.0	4.4
16/0.2	0.5	3.0	3.6
24/0.2	0.75	6.0	2.4
32/0.2	1.0	10.0	1.78
1/0.8	0.5	–	3.6

Amplifier Power

Although the production of the magnetic field is entirely due to the current flowing in the loop, obviously voltage must be present across the loop to produce the current, and so power is expended. The next consideration then is whether the amplifier has sufficient power to supply it along with its other loads.

The formula for calculating power is $W = I^2 R$, where W is in watts, I in amps and R in ohms. Combining this with the earlier formula we get:

$$W = \left(\frac{\sqrt{a}}{3t}\right)^2 R \quad \text{or} \quad W = \frac{a}{(3t)^2} R$$

It may be thought that while adding extra turns increases the field, it also increases the resistance thereby reducing the current, so the two balance out. However, from the formula it can be seen that the divisor is the *square* of the number of turns. Therefore increasing the turns reduces the power.

Let us take an example. A hall has dimensions of 12 × 18 m. The perimeter run is thus 60 m plus 12 m extra for door-frames, = 72 m. From the cable resistance table, the resistance of 16/0.2 cable is 3.6 Ω per conductor per 100 m. For 72 m the resistance is thus 2.6 Ω per conductor, so a twin-turn loop has a resistance of 5.2 Ω.

The power required is the area $12 \times 18/(3 \times 2)^2$, which is $216/36 = 6$ times the resistance 5.2, which is 31.2 watts.

For a three-turn loop the resistance is 7.8 Ω. The power needed is now $216/(3 \times 3)^2 = 2.7$ times the resistance 7.8 = 21 watts. From this it can be seen that it is an advantage to use more turns if amplifier power is limited.

The three-turn loop using three-core 16/0.2 mains cable will in most cases prove the most practical. However smaller halls having a total perimeter of around 50 m would have a loop resistance of 5.4 Ω, if three turns of 16/0.2 are used. This would be rather low if the loudspeaker system is to be fed from the same amplifier. The loudspeaker impedance would have to be no less than 20 Ω if the total impedance is to be kept above 4 Ω. Using 13/0.2 cable which has a resistance of 4.4 Ω per 100 m, a total of 6.6 Ω can be obtained which permits a loudspeaker impedance of 16 Ω to match a 4 Ω output.

An alternative is to use two runs of twin cable giving four turns. With 16/0.2, the resulting resistance is 7.2 Ω which allows a 12 Ω loudspeaker load.

The ratio of loudspeaker impedance to loop resistance gives the inverse proportion of power available to each. Thus for the three-turn 7.8 Ω loop in a 18 × 12 m hall, which requires 21 watts, a loudspeaker load of 12 Ω would take $21 \times 7.8/12 = 13.5$ watts. This could just be met by a 35-watt amplifier. The resistance of the loop should always be lower than the impedance of the loudspeaker system so that it receives most current.

If complaints are received that the loop signal level is too low, the loudspeaker level can be reduced by inserting a resistor in series with the loudspeakers. The amplifier volume level will then have to be increased to provide the same sound output, and thereby the loop signal is increased. The value of the resistor will depend on the impedance of the loudspeaker system, but around 5 Ω should do the trick in most cases. It should be a wirewound of at least 10-watt rating.

Separate Amplifiers
The matching becomes easier if two amplifiers are used, one to feed the loudspeakers and the other to supply the loop. A stereo amplifier is quite suitable providing there is a balance control or separate volume controls so that the output of each can be independently set.

The mixer output and loudspeaker amplifier control need to be adjusted so that the latter is about two-thirds advanced. This enables the loop control to be set at a higher level. If it is insufficient, the loudspeaker amplifier control should be turned back and the mixer output turned up, until sufficient signal is obtained in the loop.

However, with the high outputs obtainable with modern p.a. amplifiers, and the variety of options for series-parallel connection of the loudspeakers, there is no reason why a single amplifier should not be perfectly satisfactory in most cases. A lot depends on the amplifier that is already installed in the hall, there is little point in scrapping a perfectly good one if it can be made to supply both loads.

Field Distribution
So much for the electrical features of the loop, we will turn now to its magnetic properties. The coils in the hearing-aids have a vertical axis the same as the loop and so are in effect a coil within a coil. There is thus a high degree of coupling between them. If the orientation of the hearing-aid changes, such as if the wearer bends down, the coupling is reduced and the signal fades.

Field strength within the plane of the loop varies considerably across the width of the loop as can be seen from the solid line in Figure 27. From an 0 dB level at the centre it rises dramatically to a high some 20 dB up near the loop, then plunges to 0 dB at the loop to fall to −20 dB beyond it, then rise to gradually fall off again.

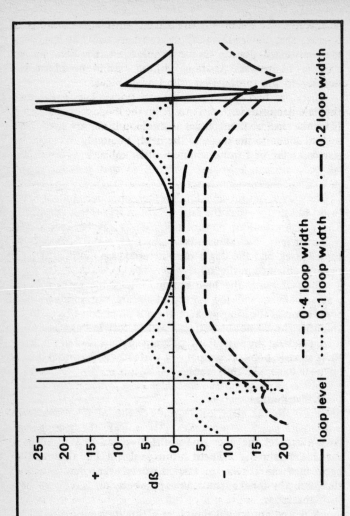

Fig. 27. Distribution of magnetic field across the loop at various heights relative to the loop. The heights, which can be above or below the loop, are given in fractions of the loop width.

Ignoring for a moment the effects outside the loop, it is obvious that the wide variation across its width is not satisfactory. Ideally, a user should be able to sit anywhere, and be able to change his position without having to adjust his hearing-aid, but this falls very short of that ideal.

There are two reasons for the variations. The first is that the field decreases with distance from the loop, so that starting from the centre, it increases as the loop is approached. The second is due to the shape of the field; it consists of a series of circular lines of force surrounding the cable, see Figure 28.

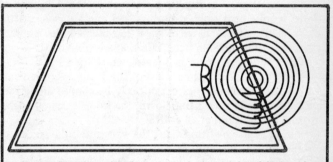

Fig. 28. The sharp drop in response in the vicinity of the loop is due to the circular nature of the field. At a distance the field is vertical and there is maximum coupling with the vertical coils of the receiver; near the loop the field changes to horizontal and coupling is at a minimum.

At a distance, the lines of force are vertical and so achieve maximum coupling with the hearing-aid coil, but close to the cable they curve away to the horizontal. This results in the sharp drop in signal as the cable is approached.

If though we move out of the plane of the loop so that we are displaced above or below it at a height equal to a tenth of the loop width, the field strength is as shown by the dotted line in Figure 27. The rise as the cable is approached is counteracted by the field curvature so that it is far less steep, and so the fall is also less severe near the cable. A slight hump and dip near the cable is the overall result.

105

At two-tenths of the loop width, the response is flat with no humps, but it begins to fall off well before the cable is reached. This is shown by the dotted/dashed line in Figure 27. At four-tenths, the fall off is still further in from the cable although it is also less steep, as shown by the dashed line. The overall level is well down and the loop needs a higher current to provide the required field strength, (see the power/height table). Note that the response beyond the loop has been omitted on alternate sides in Figure 27 in the interests of clarity.

From this it can be seen that the one-tenth displacement is the most effective as it gives a reasonably even field with a current requirement only a tenth greater and a power a fifth greater than that calculated. These can generally be ignored in practice. For medium sized halls that are around 10 metres in width, the displacement is 1 metre, which for a seated user, puts the loop at skirting board level. This is a very convenient position for installation, as it can easily be clipped along the board. If there is no skirting board, the floor is near enough, the exact height is not at all critical.

It can of course be fitted along the walls above the audience head height as it does not matter whether the loop is above or below. For larger halls, this will be necessary in order to achieve the tenth width displacement, but for smaller ones it could look unsightly and would be more difficult to install.

Where the loop ascends to cross doorframes, there is no adverse effect on the field, probably because its displacement above the user is much about the same as it is below, elsewhere. Outside the loop there is an overspill for an appreciable fraction of the loop width, though at lower levels. One user was delighted to find he could still hear the programme when visiting the toilet!

Metal objects such as chair legs seem to have little effect on the results from floor-level loops. Pickup of signal from the loop by microphone cables also seems to be negligible and tests at high gain failed to produce any trace of feedback with a reel of microphone cable placed within the loop. Once correctly designed, the loop seems to have no problems.

RATIO OF CURRENT AND POWER WITH VERTICAL DISPLACEMENT TABLE

Ratio height/width	Multiply current	Multiply power
0.1	1.1	1.2
0.2	1.25	1.6
0.3	1.5	2.25
0.4	2.0	4.0
0.5	2.5	6.25
0.6	3.25	10.6
0.7	4.25	18.0
0.8	5.5	30.2
0.9	7.0	49.0
1.0	8.5	72.2

Installation

Installation is accomplished by starting the cable at the point nearest the power amplifier and clipping it around the hall in the designated position. When crossing behind the platform, consider that participants may be wearing a hearing-aid and will need to hear what others on the programme are saying. The loop should therefore be raised so that the tenth (or whatever) displacement is obtained with the user in the standing position. This could be achieved by running it at about 1 metre from the platform floor, or if this interferes with the decor, it could be diverted to about a 3-metre elevation to give a high displacement. This would give very poor results though for a seated participant and could also affect users in the front rows, so the 1-metre position is much preferred. If desired it could be concealed by burying it in the plaster.

When returning to the starting point, the cable should be cut and both ends connected into a junction box as shown in Figure 29 if using three-core mains cable. Care is needed here because if a turn is connected the wrong way round it will subtract from the field instead of adding to it. From the two free ends a twin cable is connected to the amplifier to complete the installation.

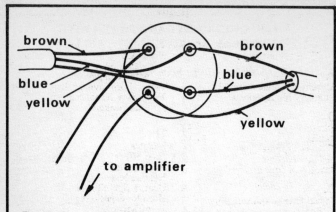

Fig. 29. Connecting a 3-turn loop of mains cable. This ensures that the current runs in the same direction. If a turn is wrongly connected it will subtract rather than add to the total field.

One problem is that potential users unfamiliar with loops are either unaware or forget the need to switch their hearing-aids to the T position. It is necessary to remind them to do this otherwise they will obviously not get the benefit of the loop. Notices should be displayed to that effect in the foyer or cloakrooms.

Index

WHAT PEOPLE ARE SAYING ABOUT THE KAPELLMEISTER SPEAKERS

* *" . . . extraordinary clarity of these speakers."*

* *"they fulfil the parameters you have set, particularly in the small room I have to use."*

* *"I was absolutely delighted with the result. The sound is comparable with speakers I sell around £2,000 per pair." (Hi-fi dealer)*

* *" . . . everyone I know have been very impressed with the results."*

* *"Congratulations on a clever bit of lateral thinking!"*

* *"Frankly I haven't found anything industry has to offer even as remotely as pleasing as the Kapellmeisters."*

These are some of the comments received from readers who have built the Kapellmeister speakers described in the book *"An Introduction to Loudspeakers and Enclosure Design"* by Vivian Capel. The speakers occupy only 8 inches by 11 inches of floor space, should cost less than £50 the pair, require only modest DIY skills to build, and as readers keep telling us, out-perform very expensive commercial units.

The design is not just another speaker-in-a-box, but an innovatory application of the transmission line principle that overcomes many of the drawbacks of this otherwise excellent type of enclosure.

The book fully describes the theory behind the design and gives full practical instructions on how to build them. It also explains pros and cons and design theory of most other types of enclosure and cross-over networks. A must for all hi-fi enthusiasts, but especially for those interested in acquiring a pair of top-class speakers at moderate cost.

BP256 - AN INTRODUCTION TO LOUDSPEAKERS AND ENCLOSURE DESIGN.
V. CAPEL   **£2.95**
0 85934 201 8   1988   178 x 111mm   160 pages

Please note following is a list of other titles that are available in our range of Radio, Electronics and Computer books.

These should be available from all good Booksellers, Radio Component Dealers and Mail Order Companies.

However, should you experience difficulty in obtaining any title in your area, then please write directly to the Publisher enclosing payment to cover the cost of the book plus adequate postage.

If you would like a complete catalogue of our entire range of Radio, Electronics and Computer Books then please send a Stamped Addressed Envelope to:

BERNARD BABANI (publishing) LTD
THE GRAMPIANS
SHEPHERDS BUSH ROAD
LONDON W6 7NF
ENGLAND